Building on
the Best

Building on the Best

An introduction to
Appreciative Inquiry
in health care

John Edmonstone (editor)

Kingsham

First published in 2006
by Kingsham Press

Oldbury Complex
Marsh Lane
Easthampnett
Chichester, West Sussex
PO18 0JW
United Kingdom

© 2006, John Edmonstone

Typeset in Minion

Printed and bound by
Ashford Colour Press
Unit 600, Fareham Reach
Fareham Road
Gosport
Hants
UK

ISBN: 1-904235-49-2

British Library Cataloging in Publication Data
A catalogue record of this book is available from the British Library

Edmonstone, John

About the editor

John Edmonstone is a leadership, management and organisation development consultant who works in the NHS, local and central government and higher education. He has held a range of line, project and human resource management positions and for the last 20 years has run a successful consultancy business, based in Ripon, North Yorkshire. He is also Senior Fellow at the Centre for Health Planning and Management, University of Keele, Associate with the Centre for the Development of Healthcare Policy and Practice, University of Leeds and Associate of Secta Consulting Ltd.

Contributors

Robin Alfred, M.Phil (Cantab), BA (Oxon), PGCertEd. works with the Findhorn Foundation Consultancy Service

Dr Alistair Baker, MB, ChB, FRCP, FRCPCH is Consultant in Children's Liver Disease, King's College Hospital NHS Trust

Theresa Douglas, BA, RGN, DN is Clinical Leadership Facilitator, Royal College of Nursing, Scotland

Hazel Mackenzie, MSc, BSc, RGN, RSCN, NCDN, PGCertEd. is Leadership Development Programme Manager (Strategic Clinical Leadership) with the Scottish Executive, Health Department, and was formerly Head of Clinical Leadership, Royal College of Nursing, Scotland

Professor Jan Reed, PhD, BA, RGN is Co-Director of the Centre for Care of Older People, University of Northumbria

Robin Shohet works with the Findhorn Foundation Consultancy Service

Jill Turner, BA (Hons), FIHM, CIHM, FRSA is Associate Director, Cancer Services Collaborative Improvement Partnership, NHS Modernisation Agency

Margaret Wright is Director of Resolution Scotland

Acknowledgements

The most formative influence of my development as a leadership, management and organisation development practitioner was a Masters programme in Organisation Development which I attended at Sheffield Hallam University in the mid-1970s. In common with many others, I was originally attracted towards OD as a practical expression of values which had emerged in society and organisations during the 1960s and 1970s and which can best be described as humanistic, optimistic and democratic. OD was concerned with finding means of "operationalising" such values in the settings of work organisations. Yet while I was a student on the Masters programme, a reaction set in and critiques emerged of the supposed naivety of such an approach, which (it was alleged) ignored the realities of power in organisations (and in society as a whole). Phrases such as the "love/trust" model of OD and of OD practitioners as "organisational social workers" illustrate the power of a backlash which emerged strongly in the early 1980s and which (until recently) has never really retreated – so much so that in the mid-1990s I co-authored a journal article titled "The Death (and Rebirth?) of OD". There seemed to be little connection between the original values of OD and what my co-author and I identified at that time as:

- The determination of personal and organisational success purely in "business" terms.
- The focus of change activity towards short-term and tightly-prescribed ends.
- The fostering of "unitary" frame of reference where OD was simply an instrumental tool used as a means to move people towards ends which they had no say in defining and to which they felt little identification.
- The resulting transformation of the OD practitioner role from that of a "scientist" to that of a "technician".

Gradually, though, from involvement in large group interventions such as Future Search and Open Space, I began to reconnect with the original values of OD and eventually, from a period of working for three years part-time with the Centre for the Development of Healthcare Policy & Practice at Leeds University, I began to explore the world of Appreciative Inquiry. I came to see how OD itself was bound up with the dominant paradigm in social science (indeed in science generally) and that Appreciative Inquiry offered a way of working that was indeed truly humanistic, optimistic and democratic – and which worked amazingly well in releasing the optimism and energy of those engaged in it, as a powerful means of countering the cynicism which forms a major part of organisational life in many health care organisations.

So acknowledgements are due to my old colleague, Maggie Havergal, for developing our own critique of where OD had got to; to Gayle Garland at CDHPP who introduced me to Appreciative Inquiry; to my colleagues in the "partnership working group" (Jacinta Elliott, Reg Walker, Shani Choudhari and Marion Gray) where, as we developed our own shared values and ways of working, we found them to be so close to Appreciative Inquiry. Thanks are also due to the contributors to this book. They are all busy people who have had to devote some of their personal time to preparing their case studies of Appreciative Inquiry in action in health care.

Thanks too to Mel Shaw at Keele University for some "just-in-time" word processing help.

Finally, my own thanks go to my long-suffering wife Carol, who is nothing less than supportive in all my endeavours.

Who should read this book

This book is aimed at a wide audience including those in leadership, management and organisation development roles at national and local levels; front line health care practitioners leading on service improvement and those involved in consultancies. The book will also be of value to postgraduate and post-registration programmes in health and social care.

Contents

Introduction

"Be the change you want to see in the world"

(Mahatma Gandhi)

Writing a "primer" for Appreciative Inquiry in health care is not an easy task. Appreciative Inquiry is not a methodology but a way of expanding our vision of the world to include the possible. Moreover, there is no universally-accepted method or "right" way of doing Appreciative Inquiry – no "perfect process". It is not a set of procedures applied in a mechanical way and is as much an art as a science. It has been described as:

> "a way of being, a way of looking at the world around us – a way…. of giving a performance. It demands a shift of perspective that goes far wider than our professional, business or community lives. It comes to involve not just our intellectual and even emotional processes. It commands the assent of our very spirituality, of what makes us who we are and how we are."

(Elliott, 1999)

It could therefore be seen as at least premature to offer a "recipe" for how to do Appreciative Inquiry. That is why this book begins by focusing on the underlying assumptions that differentiate the appreciative approach from what is termed the "dominant paradigm" in Organisation Development (OD), and indeed in thinking and writing about organisation and management generally. It introduces the "4D" model of Appreciative Inquiry, based on the sequence of Discover–Dream–Design–Deliver. It then goes on to look at the practicality of applying Appreciative Inquiry in a number of contexts before going on to review the use of Appreciative Inquiry in health care through a number of case studies.

What is Appreciative Inquiry?
Assumptions, organisations and change

Much of what happens in organisational life (as with life in general) is taken for granted. We seldom examine the assumptions which lie behind what is taken for granted. **Assumptions** are the set of beliefs shared within a group which cause that group to think and act in a particular way. As such, they:

- Are statements or rules that explain what a group generally believes.
- Explain the context of the group's choices and behaviour.
- Are usually not visible to, or spoken about by, group members. Rather, they simply exist and develop.
- Must be made visible and discussed before anyone can be sure of the group's beliefs.

Assumptions are important because organisations tend to change in the direction of what they study – and what they study turns on these underlying assumptions! All inquiry – a question posed at the beginning of a meeting; the questions in a staff survey or the analysis used to redesign a clinical or managerial work process – is "fateful" – it plants the seeds of the future.

■ Traditional assumptions about organisations

There is certainly no shortage of models, theories and frameworks to explain planned change within (and between) work organisations. These approaches (in various forms) typically follow the sequence of:

- There is a felt "need" – a **problem** is identified
- The problem is **defined** and **analysed**
- Possible **solutions** to the problem are **analysed** and **prioritised**
- **Action planning** takes place
  - future **goals** or **targets** are set
  - **strategies** are devised to achieve these targets

- **Action** takes place – obstacles are overcome in order to achieve the desired change.

The basic assumption lying behind this problem-solving approach to change is that an organisation is **a problem to be solved.**

Yet this way of working has a number of pernicious side-effects:

- People spend their time focusing on *what is not working*. As a result, their morale tends to be reduced and they become resigned to what might be termed a "problem-filled" work environment.
- Where data-collection takes place it tends to focus on failures, with what has "gone wrong". So failure is *amplified* and leads, over time, to an unconscious air of disempowerment and inferiority. In such a setting, people tend to avoid risk-taking.
- Addressing problems in this way creates a culture of *problem-centred* improvement. The only time people pay attention to learning is when they are deemed to have "failed". This makes the development of a culture of continuous learning and improvement very difficult.

Among the consequences of this traditional set of assumptions about organisations and how they operate is the creation of **languages of deficit** to describe inadequate performance at individual and organisational levels. While some words like "the", "at" or "on" are effectively neutral, others carry a powerful emotional meaning.

Consider these words and phrases as a vocabulary of **individual deficit**:

"Stress"
"Depressed"
"Mid-life crisis"
"Male menopause"
"Obsessive-compulsive"
"Neurotic"
"Low self-esteem"
"Paranoid"
"Identity crisis"
"Dependent"
"Post-traumatic stress"
"Counter-dependent"
"Dysfunctional"
"Difficult personality".

Or these which form a (larger) vocabulary of **organisational deficit**:

"Organisational stress"
"Work alienation"
"Command-and-control"
"Role conflict"
"Defensive routines"
"Bureaucratic red tape"
"Theory X"
"Turfism"
"Low morale"
"Groupthink"
"Peter Principle"
"Management-staff mistrust"
"Job dissatisfaction"
"Authoritarian management"
"Executive burnout"
"Inter-group conflict"
"Structural inflexibility"
"Interpersonal incompetence".

This approach to planned organisational change effectively:

Defines problems
Fixes what's broken
Focuses on decay.

These assumptions form what has been termed the "dominant paradigm" and underlie much of the conventional OD interventions which have been in use over the last 40 years (French & Bell, 1999), such as gap analysis, SWOT, force field analysis, process design, etc.

A phrase often used in work organisations is that "We learn from our mistakes", but working this way means that all we can learn from mistakes is what *not* to do again!

It is important to remember that the ingrained beliefs and models of this dominant paradigm are, for many people, "wired-in". They are not easy to examine and people often have a high stake in rationalising what they have always believed, finding it hard (even in some instances impossible) to expand their vision in the way the Appreciative Inquiry proposes.

"If it were not for the Poetic or Prophetic Character the Philosophic and Experimental would soon be at the ratio of all things and stand still, unable to do other than repeat the same dull round over again."

(William Blake: "There Is No Natural Religion")

The assumptions behind Appreciative Inquiry

"We are what we think. All that we are is arises with our thoughts. With our thoughts we make the world."

(Buddha)

Appreciative Inquiry is based upon a quite different set of basic assumptions. One of these is what has been called the "heliotropic hypothesis", which asserts that social and organisational forms evolve towards images that are positive, affirming and life-giving. As a means of changing organisations, therefore, the conscious evolution of positive imagery is a real and viable option. Appreciative Inquiry assumes that:

- In every society, organisation or group, *something works*.
- *What we focus on* becomes our reality, we filter-out much of the rest.
- Reality is created *in the moment*, and because there are many of us there are multiple realities.
- The act of *asking questions* of any organisation or group influences that organisation or group in some way.
- People have more confidence and comfort to journey to the future (the unknown) when they carry forward into that future *parts of the past* (the known).
- If we carry parts of the past forward, they should be *what is best* about the past.
- It is important to *value differences*.
- The *language* we use creates our reality.

Appreciative Inquiry assumes that positive learning and innovation comes from studying, adapting and replicating best practice, i.e. what works. It serves to dismantle ingrained organisational habits of mistrust, animosity and blame and to replace them with a willingness to learn, with mutual respect and co-operation. It is concerned with:

- **Finding what works** – appreciating and valuing the best of "what is"

- **Amplifying what works**
  - Envisioning what "might be"
  - Dialoguing about what "should be"
- **Focusing on "life-giving" forces**
  - Innovating what "will be".

The "principles" of Appreciative Inquiry could therefore be summarised as:

- **Appreciate** the best of what exists and people's hopes for the future.
- **Apply** knowledge of what works and what's possible.
- **Provoke** the imagination regarding new ways of organising creative improvements.
- **Collaborate** through collective capacity-building and share expertise and resources.

Rather than seeing an organisation as a problem to be solved, Appreciative Inquiry sees an organisation as **a miracle to be embraced and appreciated**. It offers an opportunity to break away from the now increasingly incremental, problem-based diagnosis/treatment frameworks of OD and to move towards a fresh perspective which simultaneously addresses issues of culture, structure and strategy in ways which well reflect the original underlying humanistic, optimistic and democratic values of OD. Appreciative Inquiry provides the OD practitioner with an opportunity to reframe his or her philosophical stance – to be deliberately hopeful, to work with optimism, to create opportunity and to celebrate the human spirit in change. It does this by creating conversations that generate images of hope and vitality, based upon identifying and learning from real moments of successful interactions across barriers of economic status, hierarchy, culture and gender.

So Appreciative Inquiry diverges from conventional approaches in two major ways.

Firstly, it avoids the preoccupation with "problems" and deficiencies which generate a culture of negativity, exacerbated by the fact that the same or similar problems keep re-occurring, often with more ingenuity than those seeking to solve the problem can mobilise! Appreciative Inquiry instead finds out what is good about the present – what works well – and what makes that possible. This is the distinctive focus of Appreciative Inquiry and it unlocks energy and enthusiasm for seeing issues "sideways-on" and excites the imagination of everyone involved.

Secondly, Appreciative Inquiry emerges from a social and philosophical basis which is significantly different from the mainstream. Conventional "objectivist" thinking (the dominant paradigm) assumes that human nature and social and psychological reality is deterministic and predictable – something fundamentally stable, enduring and "out there". Appreciative Inquiry, on the other hand, holds that everyday reality (including scientific knowledge and "received wisdom") is *socially constructed* – a realm of meanings and particular ways of understanding that varies between cultures and changes through time (Garvey & Williamson, 2002). It is a product of the moment and so open to continuous reconstruction. Language itself is a form of social action; asking questions changes how we see things and how things are expressed powerfully influences how we think about them. Moreover, because our reality is socially constructed, we have *choices and options* which derive from our questions and action. Seen from this perspective, the dominant paradigm has constructed a "rear-view world" where the underlying logical positivist assumptions (and the methodologies based upon these assumptions, including "mainstream" OD) tend to create, recreate and sustain the social realities they purport to be studying and seeking to change.

The term Appreciative Inquiry is carefully chosen. The Collins Concise English Dictionary offers the following definitions:

> **Appreciate**: to think well of; to enjoy or esteem; to recognise gratefully; to estimate the quality or worth of; to be fully or sensitively aware of
> **Inquiry**: the act of exploration and discovery; asking questions; being open to seeing new potentials and possibilities.

Appreciative Inquiry does not, however, mean "uncritically positive". It is not about avoiding or denying bad news. It is quite deliberatively called the *appreciative* approach – not the affirmative approach or the positive approach or the uncritical approach. It does not assume that "everything is for the best in the best of all possible worlds", but instead recognises that positives and negatives are mixed in unequal proportions in everything we experience. However, it also asserts that we can *choose* the elements in the situation we want to work with – and that there are real advantages in choosing to work with what works – that we can build on the best!

To summarise then, what makes Appreciative Inquiry different is:

- The framing of questions and issues in *positive terms* as its distinctive feature.
- The *inclusive approach* adopted to all stakeholders.

- The *appreciative*, but not uncritical, *focus*. It is not about either denying or avoiding bad news. It is about working with those elements in a situation which have the greatest *potential*.

These differences between Appreciative Inquiry and the more traditional approach to organizations and people can be summarised as follows:

Traditional approach	Appreciative Inquiry
Focuses on problems	Focuses on possibilities
Problem-led	Future vision-led
"What problems do you have?"	"What is working here?"
Expert-led	Self/team/organisation-led
"The glass is half-empty"	"The glass is half-full"

The key to successful use of Appreciative Inquiry is not to claim that the current way of seeing the world (the dominant paradigm) is wrong, but to help people to realise that we may all be limited and constrained by our inability or unwillingness to see and work with larger and more expansive realities.

The **potential outcomes** than can be produced by the use of Appreciative Inquiry are therefore:

- A change in basic orientation from being problem-focused to being **possibility-focused**.
- A clarified or enhanced **sense of identity** and a fostering of **shared values**.
- The establishment of a climate of **continual learning and inquiry**.
- The renewal of group **energy, hope, motivation and commitment**.
- An increase in **curiosity, wonder** and a **"reverence"** for life and work-colleagues.
- A decrease in hierarchical command-and-control decision-making and an increase in **more egalitarian practices** and **self-initiated action**.
- Improved **working relationships** and **conflict-resolution**.
- Whole-system changes in **culture and language** (an increase in co-operative practices and a decrease in competition; and increased ratio of positive to negative comments; an increase in affirmative questions and/or narrative-rich communication).

2

The "4D" model of Appreciative Inquiry

■ Conditions for success in Appreciative Inquiry

Appreciative Inquiry will work more effectively in some organisational contexts than in others. There are certain conditions which are likely to promote such effectiveness. They are:

* In work contexts, it is essential that the organisation or team is clear about *what it wants the subject of inquiry to be* – the particular topic, theme or issue to be addressed. Ideally, that subject should have been arrived at by prior wide consultative process. Appreciative Inquiry cannot work as a "mask" for already-made senior management decisions. The topic must be something that the team or organisation wants to learn about and to enhance their way of working on. Appreciative Inquiry often seems to work better with "people" issues rather than issues of technology, information, etc.

* There must be commitment to a *genuinely participative process* that includes, at least conceptually, all the various stakeholders – including all the staff who will be affected and those normally "on the margins" whose voice would otherwise not be heard. It will obviously involve, for example, professional associations, trade unions and various interest groups. It clearly helps to choose "positive" people, including supportive colleagues, friendly partners and concerned service users/carers. Experience suggests that people at different levels within organisations experience Appreciative Inquiry differently. For example, senior executives often appear relieved to discover an approach which seeks to build on what is working well; middle managers see the benefit of multi-disciplinary and multi-agency communication opportunities and frontline staff see the process as a means of making their voice heard. Appreciative Inquiry also puts people back in touch with why they started off doing what they're

doing and why they continue to do it – with particular emphasis on what they feel passionate about and why.

- *Process integrity* – or a matching of ends and means. For example, if the focus is the development of more integrated working between different professions and occupations and greater devolved decision-making, then the Appreciative Inquiry process needs to involve people in discussions across professional, functional and hierarchical lines, and frontline staff must have a powerful say in how the Appreciative Inquiry process is managed.

- Everyone concerned in the Appreciative Inquiry process (or who acts as a "gatekeeper" to enable it to happen) must be prepared to make the *effort*, put in the *time* and *work* to give the process a reasonable chance. Although the principles are simple, this does not mean that results will necessarily come easily. Appreciative Inquiry is not a "quick fix" – it takes time.

- Participants in the Appreciative Inquiry process need to have the *courage* to trust one another. There needs to be sufficient levels of trust for people to go with the process and its (unpredictable) outcomes, which are not "plot-able" in advance. Appreciative Inquiry is a journey, not a destination. The trust that is needed is not a mindless or responsibility-less trust, but a critical, challenging and searching trust. Some organisations and teams may be so full of deeply-held and unexpressed resentment and pain that they will not therefore tolerate Appreciative Inquiry unless and until there has been some prior expression and forgiving of those resentments.

- Appreciative Inquiry is not a substitute for day-to-day operational management, but it can make a significant contribution to *setting strategic direction*. Nor is Appreciative Inquiry something to be adopted when an organisation or team is in crisis. It is no panacea or "single-bullet solution".

- Appreciative Inquiry works well with *smaller teams and groups.* The larger the organisational focus the greater the problems of ensuring genuine participation in the process by all stakeholders and also of ensuring sufficiently sensitive analysis of the data generated. Nevertheless, creative designs, such as the Appreciative Inquiry Summit, can engage the involvement of larger groups of people.

- When the going gets rough, there is a need to *persevere* with Appreciative Inquiry principles.

By implication, therefore, it would **not** make sense to use Appreciative Inquiry in situations in which:

- Predictable and linear processes and outcomes are required.
- Structured problem-identification and problem-solving of "tame" problems is the preferred method for change, rather than the addressing of "wicked" issues (Rittel & Weber, 1973).
- There is lack of support for the inspired self-initiative and passionate dreaming which Appreciative Inquiry fosters.

■ The 4D model

On that basis, Appreciative Enquiry is based on what is often called the "4D" model, as shown in Figure 2.1.

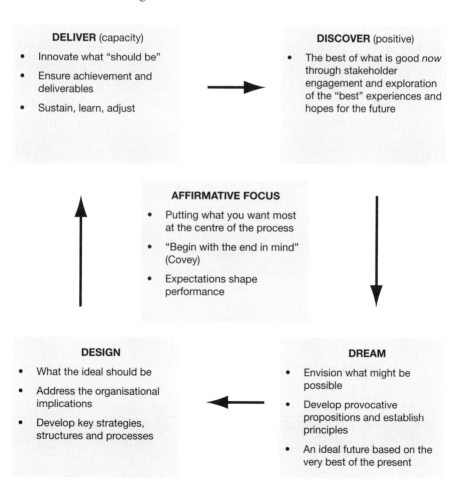

DELIVER (capacity)

- Innovate what "should be"
- Ensure achievement and deliverables
- Sustain, learn, adjust

DISCOVER (positive)

- The best of what is good *now* through stakeholder engagement and exploration of the "best" experiences and hopes for the future

AFFIRMATIVE FOCUS

- Putting what you want most at the centre of the process
- "Begin with the end in mind" (Covey)
- Expectations shape performance

DESIGN

- What the ideal should be
- Address the organisational implications
- Develop key strategies, structures and processes

DREAM

- Envision what might be possible
- Develop provocative propositions and establish principles
- An ideal future based on the very best of the present

Figure 2.1 The 4D model of Appreciative Inquiry

Throughout the process of Appreciative Inquiry there is what is called an *affirmative focus* – the idea of being determinedly positive and placing what is wanted most at the centre of the process. This is close to Stephen Covey's notion of "beginning with the end in mind" (Covey, 1994) and is founded on the principle (familiar to sports coaches) that expectations shape performance.

DISCOVER

> "The real act of discovery consists not in finding new lands,
> but seeing with new eyes."
>
> *(Marcel Proust)*

The Discovery phase replaces the "problem identification" activity which forms part of the traditional (and conventional) approach to planned organisational change. It is always tailored to the specific organisation, team and situation concerned. In this phase of the 4D process people recall periods of excellence and significant achievement. They identify those factors that contributed to best examples or "peak experiences". They appreciate and re-appreciate their ability to make worthwhile things happen. This can be done by a variety of means, including:

- Storytelling
- People interviewing each other in pairs
- People working in small groups
- Drawing pictures of moments of excellence and sharing the meaning behind them.

The latter method is particularly useful where Appreciative Inquiry is used with people for whom English is not their first language of for whom literacy may be an issue.

Whichever method is used, it helps to:

- Assume **intelligence** and **good sense** in the person(s) with whom the dialogue is taking place.
- Focus on the **essential elements** of the story that is being told.
- **Follow what you're attracted by** – what evokes a response in you.
- Support and build-on your colleague's **excitement,** by showing your curiosity about the experiences, thoughts and feelings expressed.

- **Make notes** and pay attention to inspiring anecdotes and vivid quotations that capture or summarise something important to your colleague.
- It is important to let your colleague tell his or her story, **without interruptions**, opinions or comments. If people take it in turn to tell their stories then the opportunity for each person will occur later.

The *scope* of the storytelling, interview or discussion depends on the overall focus – the topic, theme or issue being addressed. A key question is whether it affects the whole system or only concerns certain groups. Examples could be a structural reconfiguration of services; the development of a strategic plan; the aligning of service strategy to client demand; engaging the public in local decision-making; developing partnership working or building a team. What matters most is an *inclusive approach* to involving the stakeholders, including those who often tend to be forgotten, ignored or marginalised.

Much of this process is based on questions – but *positive questions*, which illuminate, rather than stifle. The idea is to shift the emphasis from deficits and deficiencies to accomplishments and achievements. This is not an easy move to make. Figure 2.2 shows the difference between positive and negative questions.

The questioning process may need to "get beyond" and challenge some of the more obvious responses and will need to do this in a conversational manner. Self-disclosure on the part of the questioner can help here. If there are obvious differences within the team, group or organisation, it may be possible to use them to foster the questioning process – for example, by getting younger members to question older members or by getting "peripheral" workers to question "core" staff.

In asking questions, it is important not to rush or to push for answers. For example, it may be helpful, if there is no response, to rephrase the question or

Negative	Positive
"What is your problem?"	"What do you want?"
"How long have you had his problem?'	"How will you know when things have improved?"
"What difficulties do you experience in doing your work well?"	"What are your priority needs to do your work?"
"What is lacking in our policy on X?"	"What aspects of policy on X are most important to you?"
"Who is to blame?"	"What resources do you already have that can help you achieve what you want?"
"Why haven't you solved the problem yet?"	"What is the next step?"

Figure 2.2 Positive and negative questions

to move on to another question – thus not belabouring a question which does not generate a good response. If the individual does not respond, then the problem probably lies with the question, rather than the person!

Some of the questions which can usefully be asked are:

- **Self:**

  "Reflecting on your experience to date, with all of its ups and downs, what have been the high points? Choose one when you felt you were really making a difference – when you felt most committed, most connected, most fulfilled and most alive in your work. What were the circumstances? Why did it feel good? Who were you working with? What did you achieve? What was special about this experience?"

  "Without being modest or humble, what do you value most about yourself (your distinctive competence) and your work?"

  "What gives "life" to what you do – the core, energising factor?"

- **Team**

  "Describe a time when you feel the team performed really well – a high point – and you were proud to be a team member. What were the circumstances during this time? Who was involved? What were you doing? What were other people doing? Why did it work well? Why were you proud?"

  "What do you value most about being a member of this team? Why?"

  "If you could transform the team any way you wish, what would it look like? What three things would you do?"

- **Organisation**

  "Describe a high point in your experience of the organisation. When did you feel most good about working here?"

  "What is it that you most value about the organisation?"

  "What aspects of organising do we do really well?"

  "What have we got right in terms of organisational design?"

  "What are your hopes for the organisation? What "best" might it represent? What might it achieve? What does the organisation have the capacity to become?"

"What do you see as priorities? What part could you play in making these priorities happen?

"If you had three wishes that could make the organisation more vital and effective, what would they be?"

Sometimes it can be difficult to get people who work together to talk about the things that they hope for, but have never seen. It opens them up to ridicule and embarrassment. So it can be helpful to talk about what they have experienced elsewhere or heard or read about. Such questions are therefore about experiences and people which are **exemplars**, and might include:

"Describe a person, organisation or incident that you feel offers a great example. What were the circumstances that led to it? What were the consequences?"

"Describe a time when you were part of, or observed, an extraordinary display of successful working. What made that possible?"

Finally, it is also helpful to capture the **essence** of the dialogue, by asking:

"What is the most exciting information you've learned from this discussion? What is the best story or most quotable quote?"

Enabling questions can encourage each person to say more and open up about the particular example they are describing. These supplementary questions can include:

"Can you please tell me more about this?"

"How did that feel?"

"Why exactly did you feel like that?"

"Why was this important for you?"

"What made that situation really special so that it stands out from all the others?"

"What was your contribution in that situation? What was the contribution of others?"

"What do you think made that possible?"

"How has this changed you personally?"

"How would you value that on a scale from 1 to 10, where 1 is poor and 10 excellent?"

Some *tips for conducting interviews* at this stage include:

- *Let the interviewee tell his or her story*. Don't tell yours or give your opinion about their experiences. Suspend your own assumptions or judgments about their experiences.

- Be genuinely *curious about the interviewee's experiences, thoughts and feelings*. Try to go beyond the superficial, like a child with a sense of wonder.

- Some people will take longer than others to think about their answers. *Allow for some silences.*

- Tell the interviewee that you will keep the information they provide, and the conversation, *confidential*. You will use the data, but it will be compiled into themes using data from their interview and others. No names will be associated with any overall summary or report. Stories and quotes from interviews may be used without a name associated with them.

- If someone doesn't want to, or can't, answer any of the interview questions, *go on to another question.*

- The *interview "rhythm"* should move from the interviewee's specifics of particular situations, occasions and times to generalisations by the interviewee about organisational or team conditions, factors or forces that may have fostered or nourished those peak experiences.

- Take good *notes* and listen for great *quotes and stories.*

- *Watch the time*. The interviewee's story may be fascinating, but you also have to manage the time. If you feel that you are learning so much that it is OK to run over the agreed time-limit, then check that out with the interviewee also.

- It's a *conversation* – be yourself and have fun. If the interview is approached as a piece of drudgery then it has failed before it has begun. Rather, consider that for the duration of the interview the interviewee is your teacher and you are the learner.

These interviews and discussions are not soliciting facts and opinions so much as examples, stories and metaphors – the particular rather than the general – the purpose being to locate those moments, events and stories of the best there is.

What emerges from these conversations in pairs or small groups then needs to be shared with larger groups in order to discover, when people performed well, what were:

- the **common circumstances** in which they did so?
- the **common topics, themes or issues** which ran through the stories and "bound" them together?
- the **core values** which were exemplified?

Finally, these findings have to be collated, sifted and summarised. One way of doing this can be to create a matrix which has as one dimension the elements of organising that might need to be developed (teamwork, leadership, empowerment, etc) and as the other dimension the particular groupings it might be helpful to focus on. This is shown in Figure 2.3. However, the participants in the Appreciative Inquiry process will need to be consulted on how this data should be interpreted. If this Discover phase is rushed or incomplete, then a trap awaits the remainder of the process, because it may be perceived as either (on the one hand) "politicised" in order to produce what the organisation wants, or (on the other hand) "pie-in-the-sky" and totally unrelated to people's everyday experience.

Time spent at the Discover phase of Appreciative Inquiry – at the "front-end" of the process – will be directly reflected in the quality of, and commitment to, tangible actions at the end of the process.

	Teamwork	Leadership	Empowerment
Levels			
Sites			
Professions			

Figure 2.3 Appeciative Inquiry matrix

DREAM

"Whatever you can do or dream you can begin it. Boldness has genius, power and magic in it."

(Goethe)

This phase replaces the usual "problem analysis" or "seeking alternatives" step of the conventional approach to planned organisational change and involves using past successes to envisage a desired future. The choice of "Dream" rather than, say "Develop" is important – the language used in Appreciative Inquiry is different from that in much organisation and management, such as strategic planning, benchmarking, problem-solving etc, all of which are redolent of the vocabulary of organisational deficit highlighted in Chapter 1. This language is more inclusive of whole-life issues, rather than the narrower perspective of work and organisations. This is a time, instead, for people to think big; to think "out of the box". Appreciative Inquiry inspires, stirs feelings and promotes curiosity. The "ideal" is grounded in the best of **real** experience, and so represents compelling possibilities. A useful way to describe this is:

"These are the dreams that we see in the day-time that we can believe in achieving, rather than the dreams we see at night which vanish with the dawn."

The Dream stage involves writing **"provocative propositions"** – statements that bridge the best of "what is" with speculation or intuition of "what might be." They sum-up what needs to happen to make it possible to deliver the dream and which form the guiding principles for the Design stage. They are provocative to the extent that they stretch the realm of the status quo, challenge common assumptions and help to suggest real and desirable possibilities for the team or organisation. The purpose of these provocative propositions is to keep our "best" at a conscious level. They are a way to describe organisational patterns and symbols and are derived from stories and discussions about what actually took place in the organisation. They are statements of the organisation or team aspirations and intent which are based on an analysis of the team or organisation at its best. In many ways, developing provocative propositions is like architecture. The task is to create a set of propositions about the ideal organisation or team – what would it look like if it were designed to maximise and preserve what has emerged from the Discover phase?

The process that is followed involves:

- Finding examples of the "best" from the dialogue in the Discover stage.
- Determining (in detail) what circumstances made the best possible.
- Taking the stories and discussions and envisioning what "might be" in order to write provocative propositions that describe the idealised future *as if it were already happening*. This "what if" process needs to be applied to all the common themes, topics and issues identified in the Discover stage. Provocative propositions should excite, guide and stretch the participants towards the preferred future.

A useful checklist for reviewing provocative propositions is:

❑ Is it *provocative*? Is it innovative? Does it stretch, challenge or interrupt?
❑ Is it *grounded* in examples of what we know we can do at our best? Are there examples that illustrate the ideal as a real possibility?
❑ Is it *what we want*? Will people defend it or get passionate about it?
❑ Is it stated in *affirmative*, bold terms and in the present tense (as if it were already happening)?
❑ Does it secure people's *involvement*?

Examples of provocative propositions are:

"This NHS Trust makes explicit its commitment to real clinical leadership by enabling all clinical directorate teams to control 75% of all budgets and resources by the end of the next financial year."

"The Nursing profession in this Trust makes real its commitment to empowerment of frontline staff by creating, resourcing adequately and supporting a system of Shared Governance which will become an example of best practice both nationally and internationally by 2010."

DESIGN

> "A vivid imagination compels the whole body to obey it."
>
> *(Aristotle)*

This stage is concerned with application – with determining what needs to happen to achieve the dream – but in specific, concrete and tangible terms.

It works best if energy is focused on a single clear goal around which there is consensus and which is challenging, but achievable, because it is based upon past accomplishments. This is a period of hard work on *"co-creation"* as working parties, project teams, task forces and so on voluntarily work to "make it happen", with an emphasis on working-through in a practical manner the transitions which are needed in order to achieve the provocative propositions. Moving from the Dream to the Design phase requires the consultant/facilitator to have an excellent working understanding of the local organisational arrangements, so as to be able to work with the organisation or team to craft realistic and "do-able" actions that also reflect the provocative propositions of the previous phase.

Key questions here include:

"What would help us to achieve more?"

"What would be the ideal state of affairs?"

"If we redesigned our structures, procedures and processes, what would really delight and benefit our users/patients/clients?

"What would our work look like if we redesigned it around the things we truly value?"

"How can we make it work?"

"What conceptual, behavioural and operational changes will we need to make?"

"Who do we need to link up with and have a connection with that we don't currently do?"

"How could we learn more from people in the team/organisation?"

"What further work or research might we need to do in order to refine our ideas?"

It can often be useful to use a generic model like the 7-S approach (Peters & Waterman, 1982), which encourages practical consideration of the various significant elements:

1. *Shared Values*: The set of beliefs that "binds and bonds" the team or organisation together
2. *Strategy*: The general direction the organisation or team will need to move in.
3. *Structure*: The active network of roles and relationships

4. *Systems:* The ongoing procedures that enable the organisation or team to function.
5. *Staff:* People and their individual and group needs for development and motivation.
6. *Skills*: The competence needed by the people in the organisation.
7. *Style*: The idiosyncratic local approach taken to communication, leadership, etc.

Action planning is central to this phase and this involves "dis-aggregating" actions into:

• *Short-term*: Say, next 3 months.
• *Medium-term*: Say, 4-12 months.
• *Longer-term*: Say, over 12 months

and deciding *who* needs to do *what, where, how* and *by when*. Arrangements for the day-to-day *steering* of the work and the means of *reviewing progress* on changes will also need to be considered at this point.

Where task forces or project teams are formed, this (of course) needs to be done on the basis of a combination of voluntarism, expertise and personal interest.

DELIVER (and REDISCOVER)

"There is a tide in the affairs of men
Which, taken at the flood leads on to fortune;
Omitted, all the voyage of their life
Is bound in shallows and miseries."

(William Shakespeare: "Julius Caesar")

This stage is concerned with people collaborating together in order to sustain the dream – with pursuing action at individual, team and organisational levels; with forging links; with developing new and innovative ways of working; with experimenting; with listening to new perspectives; with mobilising support and resources for continuing improvement and innovation, and with setting new standards for what is acceptable. Most importantly, it is concerned with individuals making personal, yet public commitments to pursue particular action steps.

Key questions here include:

"What would key measures of effectiveness be? What key achievements, initiatives, processes, services and relationships should we be measured on? By whom and by when?"

"How would we know, recognise or acknowledge what has been achieved?"

"What quantitative and qualitative benchmarks would show improvements?"

"How can we communicate these intentions? To whom? By when?"

"What are the steps which I need to take as an individual to contribute to where we're heading?"

> "The best way to predict the future is to create it."
>
> *(Peter Drucker)*

3 Applications of Appreciative Inquiry

The case studies in this book detail recent applications of Appreciative Inquiry in health care. This chapter focuses on two other applications – team development and the Appreciative Inquiry Summit – and also explores "appreciative process" or the implications of Appreciative Inquiry for the consultant or facilitator. However, Appreciative Inquiry can also be used for such activity as developing a vision or mission statement (in a much more meaningful way than is usually the case) and also for identifying process enhancements and service improvements.

■ Team development

There are already ample questionnaires, profiles, etc associated with the development of team-based working. What is the added-value that Appreciative Inquiry can bring to this area? True to the approach outlined in this book, the *"Best Team" method* offers an alternative to the more conventional approaches. It involves a consultant or facilitator working with members of a team in the following manner:

- Asking all team members to recall the *best team experience* that they have ever been part of. This may relate to the current team they are members of or may refer to another team experience.

- Asking each team member in turn to *describe that experience*, while the rest of the team engages in dialogue with the "focal" person, using positive questions drawn from the Discover phase of Appreciative Inquiry.

- The facilitator's role is to encourage individuals to set aside any clichés and preconceptions and to stay grounded in the *actual experience* of the best team – to fully explore what it was about themselves, the situation, the task and other team members that made it such a peak experience.

- The facilitator asks the team to develop and list, on a consensual basis, all the *attributes of an effective team* on the evidence of what they have heard.

- The facilitator then asks the team members to publicly acknowledge *what they have seen others in the team do* that has helped the team to be more like any of the listed attributes.

- Each team member then spends about 5 minutes thinking about *what they have done personally* to help the team to be more like those attributes – and then reports this to other team members.

The Best Team approach can be used as a precursor to other, more focused approaches to team development. It is particularly helpful with newly-formed teams and can help the "norming" process whereby initial team values and early working rules are established. The penultimate step in the Best Team approach of publicly appreciating other team members' positive behaviour may, however, not always be appropriate with such newly-formed teams (they may have little practical evidence on which to base such comments) and this element may perhaps be introduced later. The Best Team approach can also have useful applications with:

- Teams who are aiming for more effective working.
- Project teams who are facing major challenges
- Teams which require renewal, re-energising and the development of a clearer focus.

■ Appreciative Inquiry Summit

Recent years have seen the growth of large group events in Organisation Development which seek to get representatives of the whole system in one place for a significant period of time in order to take a comprehensive and inclusive approach. Examples of such large group events include Open Space, Future Search conferences and Real-Time Strategic Change. Appreciative Inquiry contributes to this "school" of approaches through the *Appreciative Inquiry Summit.*

The Appreciative Inquiry Summit is a large group event (from 50 people upwards) which runs for up to four days and which, while adopting elements of other approaches, is firmly based on the 4D model – that is, it is fully affirmative. Typically, prior to the event itself the Discovery phase has been undertaken by collecting the stories of people across the system and the results of this data-collection will form the basis for the Summit, which concentrates on the Dream and Design phases. In particular, the Summit identifies those things across the system which need to be *preserved* – the significant practices and traditions that need to be maintained as the system changes.

The Appreciative Inquiry Summit has applications in such areas as strategic planning on a whole-system basis, organisation or system re-design, post-merger integration, the reconfiguration of services and as an "umbrella" for multiple change initiatives in a system. As with other large group events, it requires significant facilitator resourcing to support the numbers of people involved. Among the outcomes of the Appreciative Inquiry Summit are:

- Change is perceived as "real work".
- The development of a whole-system "mindset".
- Creation of a critical mass of people making changes which they believe are needed.
- Rapid, whole-system, simultaneous action and implementation.
- More informed and more effective change efforts.

■ Appreciative process

Working with Appreciative Inquiry has important implications for the consultant or facilitator. They need, for example, to help an organisation or system to find their own Appreciative Inquiry approach – one that meets their idiosyncratic situation and requirements – rather than offering a "package". While most facilitators have well-developed active listening skills, with Appreciative Inquiry there is an important shift in focus in terms of what they are listening *for*. So, facilitators also need to develop their personal orientation or *"appreciative process"* by paying attention to what is already working well – those aspects of, for example, leadership or team working that people want to see more of. Facilitators have a role, therefore, in helping people to become aware of how good things currently are, and in framing, shaping and embellishing such awareness into affirming and generative images. In personal terms, this means that the facilitator has to divest herself of many preconceptions and assumptions. An open heart; a sense of what others find inspiring; an eye for beauty and a poetic ear may be just as important as analytical or diagnostic ability!

In practice, facilitators support this process by the activities of "tracking" and "fanning".

Tracking begins with the assumption that whatever the organisation or team wants more of already exists, even if in only small amounts. It involves constantly focusing attention and seeking clues for what people want more of (without any presuppositions about where it will be found) and seeing the good intentions of people in work situations. It is about not taking the every-day positive effort, skills, motivation and effort of such people for granted.

Fanning is any action which amplifies or encourages or helps to get what the organisation or team want more of. It is a form of positive reinforcement which involves paying attention and appreciating in a sincere way what has already happened – and asking for more.

The following is an example of a "Strength-Building" exercise developed by Nick Heap of New Directions based on Appreciative Inquiry assumptions. It can be used as part of team development work or other training activity.

Strength-building

Purpose

To build personal self-confidence and self-esteem.
To help people to know each other better.
To show that appreciation and being positive is valuable.

Method

The participants are in a small face-to-face group. In a larger group when time is short, demonstrate the process with one person in front of the group. Then break people into groups of four or five.

Each person has a turn of about 15 minutes as the focus of the group.

1. He or she describes an event in which they achieved something they felt good about. It does not necessarily have to be about work. Everyone else listens carefully.
2. Each group member tells the focal person two or three strengths they must have used to achieve it. The focal person then adds one or two of their own.
3. The focal person states the one strength of all those they have heard that they like the best. The facilitator can encourage the focal person to do this in a clear and positive tone of voice and posture, with no trace of self-deprecation.
4. After everyone has had a turn, ask people how they feel about themselves and the group on the basis of what they have learned.

Outcomes

People develop in self-confidence and self-esteem as they discover that their achievements and skills are valuable. They appreciate the depths in other people and want to know more. The shared and intense experience helps build group cohesion.

Using Appreciative Inquiry to initiate a managed clinical network for children's liver disease in the UK

Margaret Wright and Alastair Baker

Introduction

While the recent rapid development of paediatric gastroenterology in Wales and Scotland have resulted *de facto* in Managed Clinical Networks (MCNs) emerging in each country, the long-standing relationships and greater complexity of the larger English health care system have presented a greater challenge to this new way of organising multi-disciplinary patient-centred care. Children's liver disease is a sub-specialty of paediatric gastroenterology, but organised and funded separately in three National Paediatric Liver Centres in London, Birmingham and Leeds by a Department of Health grouping for rare conditions – the National Specialist Commissioning Advisory Group (NSCAG). Paediatric liver services in the UK have developed with adult services driven by surgical innovations, including liver transplantation, but made possible by medical developments in immuno-suppression (anti-rejection treatments) and endoscopy. Paediatric liver disease care throughout the world is often practiced as part of paediatric gastroenterology. While the two have a certain amount in common – such as endoscopy, nutritional care and some aspects of immunology/infectious diseases – they also have major differences in intensive care (ICU) involvement, the timescale for necessary clinicians' responses, and staffing levels.

Paediatric liver diseases are all uncommon and some are very rare. It is impossible for every paediatric gastroenterologist to be a completely competent hepatologist. In the UK paediatric liver services have been organised nationally (supra-regionally) through NSCAG which aims to help patients by improving access to services for rare conditions (typically less than 50 cases per year) whilst seeking to sustain high levels of expertise by preventing proliferation of too many centres. It aims to help local commissioners by smoothing-out risk, and remove from them the responsibility to plan for the un-plannable. It helps hospitals by assuring a cash flow to support rare and expensive treatments. It actively encourages providers to seek patients' opinions on services.

King's College Hospital has been funded for paediatric liver disease care since 1985, Birmingham Children's Hospital since 1989 and St James Infirmary, Leeds since 2000. In total, approximately 400 new children are referred for care in the three centres each year and 90 children undergoing care progress to liver transplantation. The numbers involved are approximately 400 new patients and 90 new liver transplants per year treated by thirteen whole-time equivalent paediatric consultants, seven consultant surgeons and their teams. Outcomes have been transformed radically since 1985 when up to 40% of children died. Currently mortality rates are less than 5% overall and 5–8% for liver transplantation. The majority of patients have long-term health needs, and families develop considerable expertise and confidence. As their role has increased in recent years, and as the social environment with respect to professionals and consumerism have changed, their expectations and contributions have become very sophisticated, representing a further layer of complexity to the system.

The majority of patients referred will develop some degree of chronic liver disease entailing long-term medications, interactions with liver services, and effects on quality of life (QoL). There are no comparative data for QoL relative to other chronic illnesses, but QoL after liver transplantation may be compared to diabetes mellitus with need for medications, regular contact with services, and outcome related to factors such as family and social support, and to level of understanding of the condition in practice – the ability to act as an *expert patient*. Patients with chronic liver diseases probably have a QoL related to severity of symptoms and inverse to social adaptation. QoL improves after transplant close to that of the general population. Mothers particularly indicate a deep impact of the child's illness on their own QoL, and the need for psychological support. (Mastroyannopoulou *et al.*, 1998; Manificat *et al.*, 2003). Life expectancy, while not yet measurable, is probably also nearly normal but shortened – also comparable with the situation for diabetes.

Managed Clinical Networks (MCNs)

All three Centres are working to (or beyond) bed capacity, despite resource allocation greater than the average for the NHS, and in response have developed means of supporting local services with joint or outreach clinics, Sharecare, 'Liver Direct' the Birmingham telephone service and programmes of local education. Parents and local paediatricians are very clear in their preference for services to be provided as close to home as possible where appropriate, and to develop skills and confidence in local facilities. Nevertheless, the focus remains institution-centred with developments planned and led from within the three Centres. Managed Clinical Networks (MCNs) are:

> "linked groups of health professionals and organisations from primary, secondary and tertiary care working in a co-ordinated manner, unconstrained by existing professional and existing [organisational] boundaries to ensure equitable provision of high quality, clinically effective services"

They are seen as one way of ensuring that organisations can work together to improve access to the service, the quality of the service, and seamless care across the primary, secondary and tertiary interfaces. They also represent the opportunity to achieve this within a multi-disciplinary forum, despite the need to sustain appropriate levels of clinical skills and expertise particularly with increasing sub-specialisation amongst the medical staff.

> "The concept of Managed Clinical Networks hopes to address the dilemma of centralisation of skills but de-centralisation of care by concentrating specialist activity, while dispersing expertise through the medical community"

> *(Boon 2004)*

In practice, the term is seen as permitting a variety of arrangements operating at different possible scales:

- Within a Primary Care Trust
- Across primary, community, and acute care within a health district
- Across a number of health districts, or a larger geographical area.

The exact nature of an MCN depends on its rationale and purpose (NHS Executive, 2000). MCNs have been initiated successfully many times within the NHS. Mental health, cardiac services, palliative care, diabetes and paediatric oncology are a few of the possible examples. Their long-term effects remain to be evaluated, with apparent lack of productiveness a concern (Ferlie & Pettigrew, 1996). Resource implications are often seen as a major obstacle to initial development or progress towards targets. The formal, informal, semi-permanent and emergent relationships of the three National centres with each other and with other multi-disciplinary groups and with user individuals as stakeholders seemed to correspond well to Watkins and Cooperrider's 'ABC model for organisational inquiry' (see Figure 4.1) (Magruder-Watkins & Mohr, 2001). Given the complexity of the current situation, the rarity of liver disease, potential conflict with other services and absence of new resources – rather than attempting to create a new organisational structure that might conflict with preferences, practices and

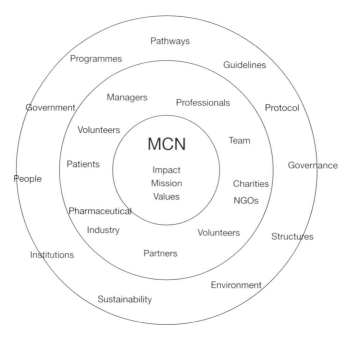

Adapted from Watkins & Cooperrider 2000

Figure 4.1 AI model for organisational inquiry

institutional politics – we wanted to establish a continuous dialogue to create alignment in core values and mission among participants in order to accommodate changes, ambiguity and imperfection in the organisational structure, while re-focusing the current relationships and practice toward better communication and patient-centredness.

The need for special skills and technical knowledge in paediatric liver services tends to amplify central influence. In recent years attempts to decentralise care have been made as described above and some gradual progress has been made. An excellent example from King's College Hospital is the nurse led Share-Care programme illustrated in Figure 4.2.

In this cyclical process, patients whose conditions are suitable for Share-Care who require frequent modifications to medication doses are identified before discharge from hospital. Following discussion with the family, the specialist nurses contact community, primary care and hospital-based agencies to request co-operation and provide the protocol. Families attend for a blood test at a time convenient to themselves (1) and the specimen is sent to be processed (2) with the result forwarded to the specialist nurses, usually by fax (3). The specialist nurses decide if it is necessary to discuss the result with a designated consultant according to a protocol and their discretion (4).

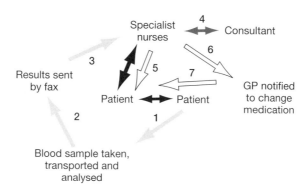

Figure 4.2 Share-care at King's College Hospital

The nurse contacts the family by telephone to discuss the result and formulate a plan, including changing the medication and when to repeat the blood test (5). The nurse notifies the General Practitioner of any change in medications in writing (6) and the GP changes the prescription (7). Key features of the process are the short-cycle time (of approximately 48 hours), the closeness to home (including much of the discussion taking place by telephone within the family's home thus reducing travelling to a minimum), the role of the family in co-ordinating the appointments locally (to give least possible inconvenience and maximum control), the contribution of professional expertise as necessary on each cycle, and the possibility to include discussions about other aspects of care and the condition during the discussions about medications. The process is therefore family-centred and has potential for communication, including feedback and learning built into it. The previous alternative involved frequent visits to the outpatient clinic in London.

The concept of *clinical micro-systems* describes a small group of people with clinical and business aims, linked processes, a shared information environment, producing shared performance outcomes and who work with a discrete sub-population of patients (Nelson *et al.*, 2002) They are complex adaptive systems and as such most do the primary work associated with core aims, meet the needs of their own members, and evolve to maintain themselves over time. It is helpful to see them as embedded in macro-organisations and the community and as part of care pathways. They are seen as building-blocks of health care and absolutely key to improving quality with patient-centred care, patient choice, and other characteristics of quality measurable and managed at this level. The Share-Care programme described above is an example of a clinical micro-system in action.

The relationships between individuals and institutions involved with children's liver disease are not embedded solely in the direct interactions around patient care. If they were, the three national centres need not interact formally at all. Apart from personal or established professional relationships, areas where important common ground or differences may arise include professional academic research and standards organisations such as the European Society for Paediatric Gastroenterology, Hepatology and Nutrition (ESPGHAN) and the British Society for Paediatric Gastroenterology, Hepatology and Nutrition (BSPGHAN) of which the Liver Steering Group undertakes regular discussions of areas of common interest. Both societies have multi-disciplinary membership, although medical and non-medical memberships are relatively separate, and the non-medical members are secondary. The College Speciality Advisory Committee (CSAC) of the Royal College of Paediatrics and Child Health undertakes training supervision, to which at least one hepatologist contributes. That representative has to canvass the views of the other UK hepatologists. The Department of Health promotes a dialogue through the Liver Transplant Advisory Group of UK Transplant that includes user representatives. It would also like to see consensus among professionals over standards and facilities. The Children's Liver Disease Foundation (CLDF) supports research with a strong bias towards medical projects based in all three national centres. Thus, there is complex on-going dialogue about the nature of services and research that is predominantly (but not exclusively) medical in agenda and language. While it involves some multi-disciplinary professionals, there is currently little direct user input, nor any plans for any increase.

■ The NHS and the context of Managed Clinical Networks

As we have seen from the definition, the concept of MCNs seeks to create a "seamless" experience of care for patients when several agencies or institutions are involved simultaneously or sequentially. The definition focuses on interactions at the boundaries between these agencies and institutions, aiming to enhance levels of expertise, roles and responsibilities on the side of the boundary close to users, including a focus on resources and accountability to users. Paediatric oncology is an excellent example of a MCN established by "conventional/traditional" i.e. top-down means. Centres wishing to be accredited as providing a level of defined service applied and were sent a very large and comprehensive list of criteria that had to be met. Protocols were provided from the central oncology centres. It was relatively explicit that there were too many peripheral centres then providing services and that those accredited would ultimately gain resources while some centres would inevitably lose the right to treat children with cancers and so lose resources.

Evidence for meeting the criteria had to be provided in an unambiguous and verifiable form. Collecting it was a massive undertaking. Inspection entailed a day-visit from a multi-disciplinary team (including parent representatives) who endorsed those parts of the service which were functioning well but made recommendations for improvements for less successful areas. The process is intended to be repeated in due course to determine progress on those recommendations.

The paediatric oncology process undoubtedly focussed departments on whether they were willing to make a significant commitment to paediatric oncology services in terms of (for example) on-call rotas and who within the department would be responsible for certain "protocolised" roles such as administering chemotherapy. However, since there were no resources directly attached to success there were no new means to remedy identified shortcomings, to buy new equipment or to develop any new roles identified as necessary. Since the inspections, the priority of oncology services within Kings College Hospital has returned more or less to its previous level. Significant changes are the increased availability of standard protocols, and chemotherapy only being given by three accredited individuals. Thus this top-down approach is very resource-intensive in preparing for inspections; tends to focus skills on a small number of individuals within the department on whom the continuation of oncology services become completely dependent and draws attention to (many) deficits without the means necessarily to remedy them. It did not look at quality of communication or evidence of "seamlessness" as contributed by the peripheral centres. Its value may be that it allows the inspectors to determine the resources and commitment of the available centres in order to reject some of them.

In September 2004, the Secretary of State for Health launched the massive and visionary 10-year programme of the National Service Framework for Children, Young People and Maternity Services (NSFC) (DoH, 2004). Key features are change in the culture of children's services toward child- and family-centredness; the concept of the child's journey; involving families in care and decisions; better information; communication; evidence-based services and quality assurance. There is also emphasis on the concept of many "small changes" implying responsibility and empowerment for gradual change at an individual or clinical micro-system level. The NSFC acknowledges changes emphasised in Shifting The Balance (DoH, 2001), decentralising priorities and decision-making but excluding the possibility of central resources. Thus, while the Government requires highly ambitious changes in services, top-down control and central resources are being withdrawn. This is the ideal circumstance for service developments using the Appreciative

Inquiry (AI) method, and one where the power of problem-solving is severely diluted.

■ Rationale for the work: background and reasons for using AI in this situation

The NHS is undergoing a critical period. Designed in the first half of the 20th century, from political and social principles developed at the end of the 19th century, it has been slow to change to provide the kind of services required by a 21st century society. Described as "drinking in the last chance saloon" (Timmins, 2002), it is receiving massive investment with organisational restructuring focused on outcomes as targets and on accountability to patients as users or consumers (King's Fund, 2001) The entire process is known as "modernisation". This broad accountability to patients (also known as "patient-centred care") will be incorporated into the organisational structure of the new Foundation Hospital Trusts through patients being the largest stakeholder group on the Board of Governors. However, "managing" accountability into patient-professional interactions will be difficult. (Maddock, 2002). Professionals tend to show allegiance to professional groups and departmental groupings, such as their ward, rather than to their hospital or its management. Poor interactions between such groups are currently spoken of as evidence of the "silo culture" of the NHS that may be a feature of clinical micro-systems in a dysfunctional macro-system. For reasons we will consider later, the development of patient-centredness may be beginning to conflict with the current culture of the NHS – with the conflict detrimental to patient care. AI is an ideal strategy for managers to exert a positive influence on professionals within clinical micro-systems toward experiential quality in professional-patient interactions (Wright & Baker, forthcoming). It may also represent a means to move beyond current conflict between silos and arising between the interests of professional groups and institutions and also occurring with attempts to develop patient-centredness. We anticipated that when staff, patients and parents were invited to recount stories about, and reflect on, when their interactions together were successful, new and shared possibilities could emerge and be made into actions by continued AI conversations.

Alastair Baker had been delegated the management of a ward which was not functioning well and without resources. There were high rates of nurse vacancy and sickness, a poor environment (particularly for cleanliness) and many clinical errors. He included ward staff in meetings including an away-day to discuss an approach to these problems, but with limited impact. Appreciative Inquiry (AI) emerged in discussions with Martin Fischer of the

Kings Fund. It intuitively seemed better than problem-solving and was worth trying. He arranged coaching in AI from Anne Radford (editor of AI Practitioner) and embarked on a series of interviews with staff on the ward. The interviews changed the atmosphere, the sickness levels and the people themselves. They had an impact at both the micro- and macro level and he was inspired by the results (Wright & Baker, forthcoming).

A different opportunity arose 30 months later when the annual meeting of BSPGHAN in Crieff provided a ready-made clinical situation to bring together AI and the current focus of the NHS on Managed Clinical Networks. A time-slot of one and a half hours was all that was available. Twenty-five people attended. The Chief Executive of the Children's Liver Disease Foundation was so impressed by the experience that she offered to support another meeting in Birmingham. This was well-attended and included very few people from the first meeting, thus spreading the awareness and impact further. The "viral" characteristic of AI resulted in a third meeting in September 2004 in London where, for the first time, young patients of only 15 years old attended and energised the process. Reports from the first two meetings have caught the imagination of a paediatric gastroenterologist who has offered to host the fourth meeting. The process' timeline is shown in Figure 4.3.

The process was designed within the constraints of time, diversity of participants and their expectations, and developed based on feedback from participants focussing on the issues prevalent at the time and depending on the resources available. When the definition of a MCN was explained it was made clear that the system was already functioning as one. We compromised between a drive to activity to obtain results (a behavioural bias in health care!), and the need for dialogue to establish common meanings and collective change. The Crieff process and structure were developed and incorporated into the next two meetings, partly to initiate participants into the AI

Figure 4.3 Timeline for the MCN process

mindset and language and partly to provide information on the work done by the previous group(s).

1. As people came into the room we asked them to find someone they did not know and to ask each other the following question for a period of 10 minutes each:

   "Tell me about a time in this network that was a highlight for you."

2. Once sufficient people to create more than two groups had joined the meeting (i.e. about 12) Alastair Baker introduced Managed Clinical Networks giving the definition specified above. Margaret Wright introduced AI as a way of talking and using questions, focussing on what worked, and which came from a desire to understand the other person's perspective. A recent article in People Management – the professional journal of the Chartered Institute of Personnel and Development (Passmore, 2003) was made available in which AI was explained as seeking to replicate what is best practice in an organisation by encouraging repeat successful behaviour.

3. Participants were then asked to join a group of their choice to discuss one of 5 topics that had been provided by email in advance. Questions relating to each topic were written on flip charts around the room and the group was asked to narrate stories of when each topic worked at its best and to note the core or essence. After 10–15 minutes participants were encouraged to distribute themselves amongst the other groups leaving one or two people to explain the discussions to new people joining the group. There was one more opportunity for people to share the work of other groups. The five topic questions were:

   • When did interactions between parents, patients and professionals created the very best experience?
   • How did protocols and standards make healthcare work at its best?
   • When did Share-Care work at its best?
   • When did education and training work at its best?
   • When did you experience referral/access to services at their best?

   Outcomes are shown in Figure 4.4.

4. From each group we asked for "one key thing that everyone in the room needed to know about the group's discussion", rather than full reporting (Figure 4.5).

1. **When interactions between parents, patients and professionals created the very best experience.**
    Talk to children
    Easy access to services
    Availability of knowledge (in one place)
    Being involved in process/consult critical to informed consent
    Quick – when you want it
    ?? – inclusive, don't feel bad about asking.
    Personal – confident in expertise, self diagnostics
    Idea: Video conferencing

2. **How protocols and standards made healthcare work at its best?**
    Have to exist – create them
    Personal opinion? – evidence base vs. 'this is how I have always done it'
    Personal prejudice
    Vested interest
    Standards/service model. Child and family-centred rather than professional-centred
    Impact of protocol (funding) – organisation/work together
    Parent input: protocol development to include all stakeholders.
    Idea: Standardisation of national protocols

3. **When share-care worked at its best**
    Use the telephone!
    Roles and responsibilities – clarity
    Communication (open channels)
    Patient-centred and family-centred approach
    Accessibility to healthcare and information
    Letters copied to all parties
    Team roles
    Key central coordinator/key worker
    Counselling
    Transition to adult services organised for optimum experience.
    Parents should hold the 'notes' so when they go to different hospitals they can keep
        people informed.
    Parents can correct typos in letters – medication taken, results
    Parents, if informed, can arrange convenient family arrangement
    To get bloods taken at night time (after work)
    Get blood results – let specialist nurses know to chase blood level notes
    In electronic swipe card
    Idea: Negotiate with parents the package they wish/want/need.

4. **When education and training worked at its best?**
    Balance: training/service
    Exposure to case mix
    Responsibility
    Maintaining skills
    Re-evaluation
    Idea: Support through networking

5. **When you experienced referral/access to services at their best**
    Support from clinical nurse specialists
    GP supportive – knew consultant's early diagnosis from GP – excellent GP referral
    Provision of information/clinical education
    Outreach clinics
    Personal welcome
    Luck!
    Idea: Parents involved in care/decisions

Figure 4.4 Summaries of topic discussions from Crieff.

From each topic group we asked for one thing that everyone in the room needed to know about the discussion in their group

Patient and carer experiences
Parent involvement – inclusiveness – family and child-centredness.

Protocols and standards
Clarity of communication.

Sharecare
Open channels.

Training and education
Balance between training, service and responsibility.

Referral and access
Education at all levels. Openness and supportive.

Figure 4.5 The 4D model of Appreciative Inquiry

5. We asked "It's 2007, what does this network look like, sound like, feel like? What is happening as a result of its work?" We logged this on a mind map after the paired discussions (Figure 4.6).

Strands are:

- Heightened awareness of liver conditions – GPs + local hospitals → Awareness of liver disease at all levels (training)
- Family accommodation at specialist centres
- Seamless – no barriers
- Equitable (and same level of care) → equity of access, parent's voice and local infrastructure, open communication, local access.
- Child-centred and tailored to family → child's own situation (transport/where relatives live/existing links etc)
- Lifelong learning/communication
- Scottish (+ Northern Ireland) specialist centre
- Nationwide electronic notes + access by parents
- Unity of approach across 3 centres → clear follow-up pathways agreed by all stakeholders
- Seamless transition of care child to adolescent to adult services via a dedicated Scottish centre! **Agreed!**
- Opportunity to network with other families – perspective
- Inclusive communications → parental access to information (quality/accurate/specific to case)

Figure 4.6 A mind map of the future for 2007

6. Participants were asked to complete a feedback form including questions about their interest in further meetings and what they had found most useful. Feedback from all 3 sessions is summarised in Figure 4.7.

What is exciting/important about the AI method?
—*Diverse but inclusive, good for communication*

What have you learned from the session?
—*Feel the same as others – professionals and parents – collective will to improve*

What was the highlight of the session?
—*Meeting new people, recognising common concerns*

What would you like to see happen as a result?
—*Development of IT for better communication*

Things that are essential to strengthening this network
—*Communication – replied by 70%*

Figure 4.7 Summary of the commonest response topics for all feedback to each of the questions from the end of all three sessions

■ Outcomes

The process to explore the interest in and initiate a MCN conforms to national specification but is better than alternatives, being user-centred and inexpensive in time and NHS resources. Parents can contribute as readily as doctors. The vision achieved was broadly agreed and without conflict. The work has attracted the interest of colleagues e.g. metabolic paediatrics. The Children's Liver Disease Foundation offered a venue for the next meeting. The format of this brief interaction was used with minimum change by Alastair Baker at the NHS Modernisation Agency Sharing Event for Critical Care in Birmingham on 5th March 2004, where the outcomes and interactions were strikingly similar.

■ Process modification for Birmingham

The Birmingham gathering started at 10.00 a.m. and finished at 4.00 p.m. and continued the conversations and learning by focusing on the "dream" phase of the AI process. Differences from Crieff in relation to the process points as above were:

Point 1. The greeting question was *"Tell about something that works for you and your part of the "system". Something you are proud of!"*

Point 5. Participants were then asked to find someone they did not know and to tell each other about this network working at its best. Some pairs finished earlier than others and were asked to write one possibility they saw for this network in the future on a "post-it".

Point 6. Participants were asked to select from 5 topics derived from feedback from Crieff written on prepared flip charts around the room. The participants divided themselves up amongst the following topics:

- Learning
- Roles and relationships
- Share-care and liver disease at home
- Access to services – first interaction
- Standards, protocols and safety.

One chance to move to another group was possible up to the lunch period.

Point 7. After lunch there was a brief introduction to the "Dream" phase of AI. The participants were invited to split into two groups with as wide a spread of experience as possible by dividing themselves into one of these categories: Consultants, Parents, Specialist Nurses, and representatives of drug companies then distributing themselves to obtain a diverse representation. A self-forming group identified themselves as "Miscellaneous", consisting of a member of the CLDF, a ward nurse and an administrator, making two groups of 8 or 9 people in each. They were asked to spend an hour and a half considering:

- **Ideal Best patient pathway**
- **When something "wrong" meets a network that works and motors along**
Or
- **A journey to "I know not where" with great company and wonderful images in a safe vehicle.**

At the end of an hour we asked both groups to focus-in on one aspect of the pathway and to add some more detail. We closed with a short comment from each group about their thoughts on this last session.

A remarkably sophisticated patient pathway with clear pointers to areas of key experiential quality was constructed (Figures 4.8a,b) A consensus over what represents the major priorities for the future, IT and customer services, was achieved. The Children's Liver Disease Foundation (who hosted this meeting) continued to be enthusiastically supportive and the process has attracted the interest of parents, professionals and the NHS Modernisation Agency. The following were agreed:

- The process be continued to include more people and to move towards design and delivery.

Group 1. Key features of the experience of quality in health care

Clarity of care pathway
Right information at right time
Welcoming environment
Customer care – pride in provision
Continuity of care – regularity/predictability

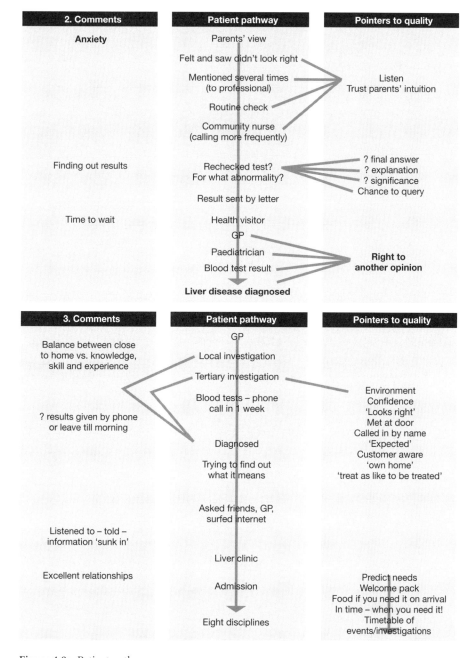

2. Comments	Patient pathway	Pointers to quality
Anxiety	Parents' view	
	Felt and saw didn't look right	
	Mentioned several times (to professional)	Listen Trust parents' intuition
	Routine check	
	Community nurse (calling more frequently)	
Finding out results	Rechecked test? For what abnormality?	? final answer ? explanation ? significance Chance to query
	Result sent by letter	
Time to wait	Health visitor	
	GP	
	Paediatrician	Right to another opinion
	Blood test result	
	Liver disease diagnosed	

3. Comments	Patient pathway	Pointers to quality
Balance between close to home vs. knowledge, skill and experience	GP Local investigation Tertiary investigation	
? results given by phone or leave till morning	Blood tests – phone call in 1 week	Environment Confidence 'Looks right' Met at door Called in by name 'Expected' Customer aware 'own home' 'treat as like to be treated'
	Diagnosed	
	Trying to find out what it means	
Listened to – told – information 'sunk in'	Asked friends, GP, surfed internet	
Excellent relationships	Liver clinic	
	Admission	Predict needs Welcome pack Food if you need it on arrival In time – when you need it! Timetable of events/investigations
	Eight disciplines	

Figure 4.8a Patient pathway

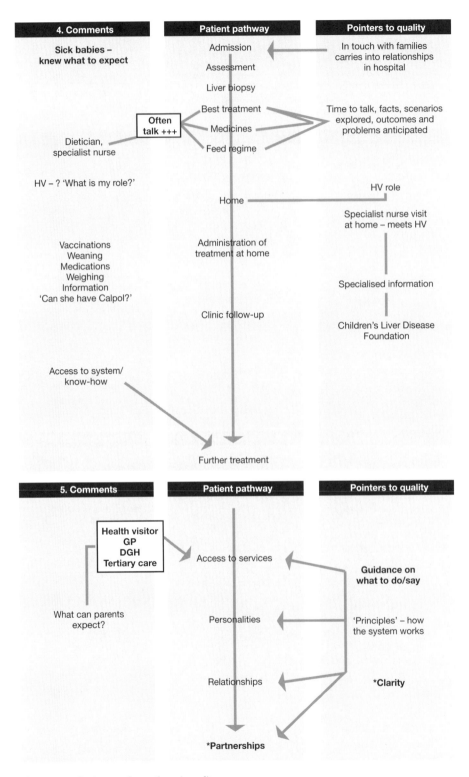

Figure 4.8a Patient pathway (continued)

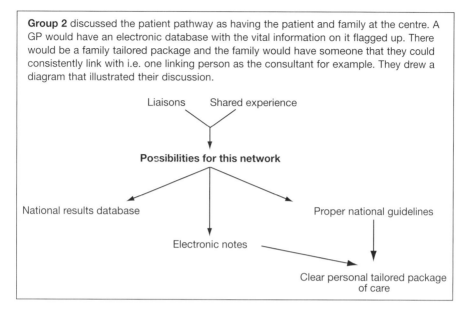

Group 2 discussed the patient pathway as having the patient and family at the centre. A GP would have an electronic database with the vital information on it flagged up. There would be a family tailored package and the family would have someone that they could consistently link with i.e. one linking person as the consultant for example. They drew a diagram that illustrated their discussion.

Figure 4.8b Patient pathway

- The events to date to be evaluated by phone calls to follow-up the outcomes.
- The results of the work to date be published and discussed as widely as possible. A paper has been published (Baker & Wright, 2004).
- The MCN to make its conclusions available to BSPGHAN both directly to council and through a new policy forum and indirectly through the Liver Steering Group to assist with policy and development.

Two group sessions after lunch looked for one hour at creating an ideal/better patient pathway from start to finish. Encouraged to take a "helicopter view" and not be overwhelmed but the size of the issue, one group chose to concentrate on first impressions, the other on the family/home. Group 1 chose guiding principles:

- **First impressions** are a key story of the first day on the ward for a member of staff.
- **Close to home** is a key guiding principle – for patients wanting treatment and care to be close to home and for professionals who would like their training and experience to be close to home.
- **Use of the Internet and cameras** could mean that there could be consultations in the patient's own home.
- **Accessibility** is key to both for people, learning and records.
- **Communications** are key – especially **continuity** of them.

- **Interaction** – between national centres – everyone needs to know and understand what is expected of them – there is an issue about standards.

During the discussion of quality in the patient pathway one parent stated that "When a consultant invites you personally into the consultation room your heart leaps." Several other people nodded assent. As a result of that feedback Alastair Baker now always invites families into consultations personally. Apart from the improved experience, no additional medical time is used as he would be waiting for a nurse to bring the family and the nurse's time can be used for other valuable tasks. A small change has resulted in all-round improvements in effectiveness of the process and its experience.

The second group discussed the patient pathway as having the patient and family at the centre. A GP would have an electronic database with the vital information on it flagged-up. There would be a family-tailored package and the family would have someone that they could consistently link with i.e. one linking person as the consultant, for example.

Feedback from the day was taken by flip chart and is summarised in Figure 4.9.

Outputs from Birmingham: April, 2004 – ideas and ways forward

- Crucial role of **GP** – but none here today.
- **Educational programme** for people to keep up to date with Liver knowledge and organisational information and practical procedures.
- Importance of **IT** to the whole system and to what people do. IT in-patient **records** and perhaps use of a **credit card** approach – you put in the card and you get all the info re. the record.
- **Video conferencing.** Could access via other agencies e.g. local schools have this and build a relationship with the hospital and the school.
- Apply **customer care principle** to health providers. Be aware of first impressions – call people by their name – first impressions arriving on a ward
- Families could have **medic alert bracelets** to alert healthcare professionals to their medical condition or treatment. The data would be available by calling the number on the disk and giving the patient's details. This is a service for which people have to pay and puts it in the hands of the patients and not the medical system.
- '**Message in a bottle'** a patient has crucial info re. themselves and their health and medication in a glass bottle in the fridge – anyone can access it and they have a notice in a window of the house so that ambulance and other emergency helpers know where to find it and can act on it and save valuable time.
- **Training opportunities** to tap into via the **drug companies**. Pharmaceutical representative offered the opportunity to join in their training and also to get ideas from them re: data sharing etc.
- Use **existing communication pathways** to share info e.g. drug companies to GPs
- Use **case histories** to reach and influence GPs – network could use the patient and other stories they have gleaned from these events to educate.

Figure 4.9 Feedback from Birmingham – Post-it ideas for service development

■ Possibilities after April 2004

Proposals for BSPGHAN

Participants were asked to consider two messages to be taken to the BSPGHAN policy meeting of June 2004 in Birmingham. They acknowledged that it was futile to ask for large amounts of resources but that emphasis on policy and perspective might yield major changes in outcomes. Their collective view was highly patient-centred and asked for the following to be considered:

1. Customer service orientation

   All participants, not only parents, expressed concern about hospital environments and lack of consistent customer service-oriented care. They wanted an emphasis on first impressions of environment and personal interactions, personalised care (including professionals knowing the name and history of patients), care as close to home as a principle for minimum travelling, and "no surprises" care – planned by negotiation, with plans adhered to.

2. IT developments

   Participants wished for more adventurous use of IT with videoconferencing allowing referrals, clinical discussions and education among professionals and ultimately "consultations in your own living room" for patients. This plan is in process toward fruition as the three supra-regional centres have obtained the funding for the equipment necessary. Communication between institutions, currently variable in quality, could be improved as a result. A National Results and Correspondence database with access by secure numbers would allow all professionals and patients access to appropriate results at any time. Nationally-accepted protocols would allow more care to be undertaken in hospitals closer to patients' homes. BSPGHAN has asked Alastair Baker to review the protocols of the three centres to consider where they can be amalgamated to initiate this plan.

Process modification for London

For the full-day London meeting elements 1 to 3 of the process were the same as for Birmingham except that Alastair Baker was able to describe eight successful outcomes of the process so far (Figure 4.10).

- Children's Liver Disease Foundation convinced – paid for a meeting
- Asked for IT facilities between units at Birmingham – it has been funded and will roll out during next year
- Need for customer services to be prioritised presented to BSPGHAN – being considered at council level
- Out-patient interactions – greet and invite families into consultations
- Design and understanding of current and idealised patient pathway
- Access to GPs through pharmaceutical companies
- This work accepted for publication
- Revealed a way of working to involve young people in creating their own services

Figure 4.10 Managed Clinical Network successes

At element 4 participants were then asked to write on a "post-it" any issue that was foremost in their minds. Topics were clustered and a number identified for immediate discussion. It was explained that there would be the opportunity in the afternoon to address three other issues of Young People's Services, Short Gut Service and London Services. Each group was asked to recount times when each topic worked best. The initial time was 20 minutes. The participants divided themselves up amongst the issues/topics. The topic headings were:

- Referral and access
- Outreach and peripheral
- Personalising care
- Education/information
- Young persons services – held over to the next session – see Figure 4.12.

Results appear in Figure 4.11.

In order to share their work and reflect on its value, participants were asked to feed- back their discussions as if to someone influential who was passing by and had just 5 minutes to spend in the room with us.

At element 5, participants were asked find someone they did not know and look to the future together for 20 minutes in total (i.e. 10 minutes each).

"In 2007 there are no constraints on you or the service. What would you like things to be like? What would you see hear and feel?"

At element 6, after a break for lunch there was a short recap of the day to help the consultants who had arrived over lunch and who wanted to focus on intestinal failure/short gut services in the afternoon to acclimatise to the group. This enabled everyone to see what he or she had achieved in the morning.

Personalising care

Positives
- Treated as an individual
- Child in an adult's body – getting balance
- Nursing staff who were interested in my life
- Play specialists – very important role
- Well prepared for transition to adult care
- Flat – good bridge to facing outside world
- Privacy

Education and training
- Keep it simple
- e-mail
- Info pack
- Study day
- MCN – identify consultants and involve them

What works now
- Parental empowerment
- Communication between centres
- Communication between doctors and patients
- Booklets/info
- Technology – can help meetings
- Relationships – staff to patients

Referral and access

Best experience!
- Communication
  - discharge letter etc.
  - speed of delivery
- IT
  - improvements
  - standardised across centres
- contact
  - communication pathways
  - named contact

Figure 4.11

At element 7 the participants then had the opportunity to imagine the future of Young People's services, London Services or Short Gut Services for 45 minutes in groups. They were asked to flipchart the conclusions as bullet points and to tell the others in the room briefly. Results for the Young People's services are shown in Figure 4.12.

As a result of the London Services discussion an annual meeting is to be organised in a conventional, but multi-disciplinary, format – focussing on education and communication. The first taking place in January 2005. The Short Gut/Intestinal failure group formed a London Short Gut Consortium who summarised their discussions as a brief paper for discussion at the NSCAG meeting 15 days later.

Idealised care

- Peer support
- Groups? Facilitated by other patients?
- Treated normally
- Not adult – not child
- Supporting parents

Idealised care

- To be treated as an individual with compassion respect and intelligence

Idealised care

- I was allowed to stay with my child whenever I wanted to
- Medical team very good at explaining information and news
- ALL procedures, however small, were explained
- Had continuity of out-patient support

Adolescents

- Adolescents want to be treated
  - as equal
  - not as children/not adult
- Workshops on ward for teaching parents of teenagers
- Teenagers don't feel it appropriate to be on ward with smaller children/babies
- Privacy

Figure 4.12

At element 8 everyone sat in a circle to consider:

"What one thing would give him or her hope that his or her ideas for 2007 would happen?"

They were also asked to consider what they individually could do to change things and to write this on a "post-it" note before they left.

The event closed with Alastair Baker thanking everyone for his or her time and hard work throughout the day. Feedback forms were distributed and received. Everyone subsequently received a report of the day.

Summary of the London meeting

Most people were meeting for the first time. Participants included patients, community nurses, hospital nurses, parents, consultants, and a GP. Five young people attended, of whom three were less than 16 years old. Their presence changed the dynamic of the gathering, and their views were particularly valuable. Those providing the service heard them first-hand for the first time.

▪ Outcomes

A further meeting was planned for Sunderland in January 2005 at the invitation of a local consultant who wishes to see and experience the process. This will mean that in a 12-month period 4 different parts of the UK – Scotland, the West Midlands, the South East and the North East will all have had the opportunity to be involved. It has attracted the interest of patients, parents, professionals, the relevant charity and the NHS Modernisation Agency. Participants (especially parents and patients) have become enthusiastic supporters, are optimistic about what will happen and want to continue.

The progress of the MCN was presented as a paper at the BSPGHAN meeting in January 2005. The aim is for this work to be the subject of action research commissioned by the Department of Health in the context of the National Framework for Children's Services. The results of the current work to-date will be published and discussed as widely as possible, particularly the agenda for customer services and IT agreed in Birmingham.

▪ Summary conclusions

This introduction of Managed Clinical Networks by AI brought many key players in health care together where they can build relationships and work to make a real difference to patients and staff. AI offers an opportunity and method for people to:

- Talk to each other in a new way, asking different questions and building relationships; identify positive aspects of their work and celebrate their achievements and successes.
- Take time to review and reflect for themselves and collect evidence of their effectiveness in a sector where the focus is always on problem-solving for others and their needs.
- Be reminded of their abilities to understand, imagine and create ideas in relation to their work environment, their work content and the way in which they do their work, thus building confidence and capacity.
- Think and be creative about their work, taking empowering actions to change things and understanding that small changes can make a big difference.

What would ideal services be like?

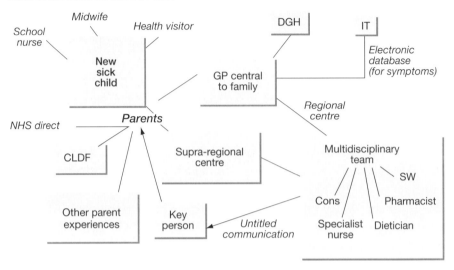

Figure 4.13 Services designed by a parent

- Identify, in a short space of time, what is important to them and what common ground exists between them and others, so enabling partnerships to be formed.

The creation of Managed Clinical Networks aims to improve services by removing boundaries and extending knowledge and involvement. The AI process has the power to re-engage and re-energise many people at the service and organisational margins of the NHS who may currently feel excluded or dependent; to involve them in the development of their own services and to invite them to look beyond the boundaries that currently constrain the development of quality in the NHS.

One parent sent us a schematised care system based on the discussions at Birmingham. It is transcribed in Figure 4.13 above.

■ Feedback interviews: what do you remember and what difference did it make?

A random selection of those who had attended the first meeting in Crieff were contacted by telephone and email approximately 9 months after the event and asked "What do you remember?" and "What difference has it made?". People remembered meeting other parents or professionals, and feeding-back to medical staff was particularly appreciated, as parents have little opportunity to meet-up with each other or professionals in the context of commenting on the service outside the specific needs of their child's care. They valued the lack of defensiveness if their comments might be seen as critical. The realisation that things do work in the current system and that there are good experiences was novel and very reassuring. Common views between users and professionals, for example the need for facilities for young people, was also recalled. Parents were struck by the realisation they were not alone in their experiences. This revelation of "Someone else knows how I feel." seemed extremely powerful and almost liberating. Professionals particularly valued hearing the opinions of parents directly and being reminded that parents' and patients' views were key to improvement. The realisation that this was part of a process rather than a meeting of a prescriptive kind was initially novel for some professionals. However even the most accomplished problem-solvers were thinking and inquiring appreciatively after about 20 minutes.

What difference has it made? Respondents emphasised the following:

- They feel more positive and less frustrated.
- They had not met anyone with a positive experience before.
- The professionals were approachable and the experience brought us closer together.
- A realisation that it is incredibly informative and fruitful to have parents and patients there and to hear their views.
- A realisation that you need to express yourself differently depending on who is there.
- Having agreed with a particular professional the benefit of a particular service development, we found it easier to ask for it for our child.
- The possibility of the supra-regional services speaking with one voice, as opposed to being seen as centres competing with one another.
- A consultant now meets and greets patients personally at the clinic after hearing a story about what a difference this makes to parents and patients.

■ The emerging future for this Managed Clinical Network and a contribution to other clinical networks

There is a need to keep all those who have been involved in the information and activity loop. The means to do this may include:

- The BSPGHAN website can be used to post information about the meetings past and future and their conclusions/outcomes.
- The findings to-date can be published in relevant journals to increase awareness.

- A further report will be made available to the CLDF for their delivery magazine.
- A seminar on Appreciative Inquiry and its application in health care could be held and include this work.
- A road-map for this MCN might include creating national practical guidelines that would help to define the network role and process as well as the role(s) of those taking part in it.
- Guidelines might (in turn) be of benefit to Managed Clinical Networks in other disciplines and fields.
- Making a modular CD video including many topics encountered in the care of children and young people with liver problems. This would involve professionals in the medical sense, but also patients and parents as experts in living with conditions and administering treatment with intimate knowledge of the way the system interacts to deliver the service.
- There may be an opportunity to use this work to contribute to the core curriculum for Inter-Professional Education (IPE) where there is discussion around communication and ethics. Alastair Baker is a facilitator on the Guy's, King's and St Thomas' IPE course.

■ Discussion

The first and overwhelming impression of the process so far is how robust it is. The introduction to AI as a 1.5 hour module of "Tell a story. Successes by themes. A mind-map of the future and Feedback" has been undertaken by us with various minor modifications on four occasions with three different professional/parent/patient combinations with strikingly similar outcomes in terms of engagement and energy, outputs, feedback and conclusions. It was consistently fun, conflict-free and energising. A few individuals carried over some skills and outcomes from one meeting to the next but are not essential for this module. A very few other individuals had difficulty in engaging, either in leaving behind problem-solving, urgency for action or "that nothing positive ever happens in my experience." They did not de-rail the process and were still included and contributed. We learned to incorporate the positive aspects of their comments in the agenda, either immediately or in the next session. It is important to channel the drive to act into planning towards an outcome to be fed-back to the group in the future, implying contact with their "real world" and creating new and functioning groupings based on the relationships created in the meeting. This module, which is relatively easy to facilitate, can create a practical vision of the future and engage many individuals with it. It is unlikely to contribute strongly to organisational *structural* change, but using AI as a tool can work well to help participants create a better achievable future that they *own*. Participants can begin to recognise that their contribution to their organisation is valuable, not only as a worker or passive recipient of care (i.e. a "cog in the machine"), but commitment beyond this in understanding, decision-making and in making "small changes" has a special value in terms of quality. Thus we have shown a valid and indeed powerful role for AI as a short intervention. We were moved to reflect that most humans are naturally good at AI.

We engaged individuals from diverse health care backgrounds and parents to generate data of extremely high quality. For example, the patient pathway drawn in Birmingham (Figure 4.8a) exhibits richness of experiential detail of quality of health care that could not be gained by process analysis from a group of professionals, no matter how diverse. Process analysis is usually considered the preserve of managers or consultants of considerable experience. Yet without such conventional "experts" a representation of an existing process combined with a vision for an idealised but achievable future was created and the participants owned and recognised it. It remains true to the principles of quality: patient-centredness, efficiency, effectiveness, safety, equity and timeliness, (Institute of Medicine, 2001) – although participants were probably not formally aware of these principles (as most UK health professionals are not). Experiences of patient-centredness can only be truly represented in any process by including the perspectives of patients. Thus, "naïve" individuals, AI, diversity and enthusiasm produced an output and understanding that it is unlikely could be achieved by a management consultancy, however renowned, using "conventional" methods. The participants worked hard to achieve it and ran out of energy by the end. We speculated that if the AI process becomes externally tasked in this way, as opposed to emergent among the participants, it becomes de-energised. It remains to be seen if these hard working participants will be affected to pursue the vision they created. This also illustrates the general principle that much more energy is available for internally-motivated compared with externally-motivated tasks.

Over three meetings, families' messages are remarkably consistent about what they wanted from services. Their requirements are reasonable and overlap with the ideals of the professionals, as illustrated by Figures 4.5, 4.6, 4.7, 4.8b, 4.12 and 4.13 – but given the method, inevitably focus on their experiences created by interactions with services, a perspective that professionals cannot know for themselves. From this data, families recognise the complexity of the system that treats their children. They accept the gradual technical developments underpinning care and are not pressing for instant massive progress. They want information and knowledge to permit involvement in decisions and to know what to expect, access to services and to be heard when they have concerns or distress, response to their concerns, trust in individuals and the system that it will work for them and it knows what is happening and what will happen. They want not to suffer unnecessarily, including from travelling or waiting – particularly waiting in ignorance. They want to feel that professionals and services recognise the unique nature of the illness and of their child and family, and respect them as individuals. They particularly want personal and equal human relationships with professionals, implying sharing power over what happens to their children. There is no evidence among these participants that they prefer dependence. They recognise that knowledge is power but also independence and promotes system reliability through accountability, and that knowledge comes from language, most easily and accurately acquired through talking, often at length, to someone whose knowledge is valued, hence they value communication. Most of these ideas are not new to health care professionals. However, they have a low priority when professionals design health care, but as we have shown, become the key principles when AI is used for system design among users.

The NHS has no tradition and poor skills in creating experiences or being aware of the experiences it creates, i.e. its aesthetics. In fact, when professionals are presented with adverse experiential data they almost always respond with denial, arguing against its validity or relevance to themselves or their departments. Alastair Baker's experience of feedback in the Birmingham meeting concerning how a short anecdote of inviting families into a consultation personalises care illustrates that AI is ideal for feedback concerning service experiences. There is no impetus for defensiveness as positive feedback is akin to praise (which does not have a strong tradition in the NHS either). The feedback was specific in terms of what behaviour made the difference, what effect it had and what future changes it idealised. It also illustrated what the parents valued in the interaction – with the possibility of creating more interactions with the same types of experience. It invited reflection on what represents excellence in health care interactions and how professionals can contribute to them. The answer in this case, as in many others, is a "small change" in behaviour brought about by a change in the professional's mental models that may be large or small depending on the professional's starting point. A major feature of these small changes (with big results) is the tendency for these changes to disregard or remove conventional boundaries. In this case the boundaries are about space and role. Alastair Baker was asked to come out of the consultation room and act as host to patients as personally recognised and esteemed visitors. Thus the professional's perspective may be dependent on his/her ideas about such boundaries. "Small things make a big difference to patients" is a reflection that emerges from AI health care interactions. (Wright & Baker, 2004). AI helps us understand that many improvements in health care quality are already in our own hands, but may confront our sense of boundaries to our professional identity. The boundaries are therefore also inside ourselves and only we can remove them.

The concept of Managed Clinical Networks implies working beyond or despite boundaries where patients' needs dictate. As it appears in the introduction to this chapter the definition does not seem very radical. However, the boundaries referred to are not only institutional (although those are difficult enough) but also inter-professional and those between professionals and patients erected to protect professionals from "sharing the anxiety associated with illness" (Menzies-Lyth, 1959) These boundaries come about during health care education via the "hidden curriculum" that is largely unarticulated, unexplored and not subjected to reflection (Crib & Bignold, 1999). Thus, in their fullest sense of overcoming these boundaries, MCNs are a very radical concept whose potential development asks profound questions about the nature of professionalism, patient-professional relationships and professionals' sense of their professional identity. The families' ideals echo these questions. Change at the level of personal and professional identity is often very difficult, especially when other vested interests such as power within and from institutions is involved. We cannot expect MCNs to be an instant success, despite their altruistic conception, and the engagement of those with a vested interest in the status quo may be a problem. AI, however, can be an optimal means to move forward. As shown in the feedback, differences between people and communication between professionals and parents are seen as intriguing and valuable. Discussions permitted common cause to be made. For example, better communication and the potential role of IT were seen as the key to a better future by 70% of all attendees. Thus AI questions current actions, roles and relationships – but without critique. It maximises the valuation of the contributions of all participants whom it values on civil equality. It answers the question "What has been done that is the best?" and invites the answers to "What can we do that is the best?" It moves beyond thinking of vested interest as a problem, to understanding that altruism and humanity, participating in effectiveness and wishing to be held in honest high esteem are important motivators to all humans.

Throughout the development of the MCN has run a strong theme of opportunism. Events occurred when and where participants could be available, by including those people who were interested and by working on themes that were generated by feedback or were in the current collective consciousness. Those topics became the agenda, but without becoming identified as problems to be solved. Funding was obtained from professional societies, a charitable source, pharmaceutical companies, a hospital and educational funds. Outcomes were aimed towards messages for available recipients such as imminent meetings of BSPGHAN, or NSCAG with respect to short gut syndrome. Thus the process has been very much "in the moment" and in and of the environment in which the participants were living and working. This approach is in keeping with the idea that one size does not fit all, in contrast to the centralised decision-making, planning, funding and execution of the NHS, with the strategy determined centrally to provide for centrally-perceived needs of patients as groups not as individuals. We also stretched the inclusiveness of the third meeting to patients, including adolescents. Five attended. Following a little hesitancy they readily contributed. Although one found it difficult, four contributed powerfully and led the agenda towards their experiences and concerns. Their ideas were simple but elegant and in no sense facile, unreasonable or irrelevant. They showed instant knowledge of how to use a mind map and could readily conceptualise a health care future. Even the young person who contributed little provided a strongly positive feedback form. It is clear that in using AI, young people (including children) can help design and create their own health care services.

A recent book (Surowiecki, 2004) argues that over time groups consistently out-perform individuals in decision-making in contexts of uncertainty, no matter how expert the individuals. However, to be so effective the groups must be genuinely diverse, with clarity of purpose and everyone must have a chance to speak. Our AI groups have been diverse by health care discussion standards. We have sought clarity of agenda, despite having partly negotiated it among participants, and it is in the nature of AI that everyone's story is heard and recorded. As with the experience of the patient pathway the explorations by groups maintain their energy and momentum best if the groups have maximum latitude for discussion and decision-making. In leaving behind the NHS model of dependency on the knowledge of the professional expert, new possibilities became evident. They are based on real experiences so a vision of the ideal future remains close to the best of what already has existed. All participants having similar health care experiences can recognise some part of that vision and adopt it in some way into their version of reality. It is a vision just a few small changes ahead of the present, created and attainable through our own collective discussions and efforts, but it is never "unrealistic" unless we slip into seeing achieving it as a problem to be solved. Facilitators can help by reflecting that improvements will be incremental (small changes), developmental, and often unexpected. The allegory of a journey is often helpful, as it is to reflect on whose destination we are travelling toward.

While in the past the NHS was thought of as a monolithic or inert institution, it seems obvious now that UK health care is more helpfully considered as a complex adaptive system. It certainly exhibits many features of complexity with uncertain cause-and-effect relationships, recurrent and emergent patterns of human responses but unpredictability including error, failure of command and control, and outputs determined by the nature of the whole system. Further features of complex adaptive systems are emergence of novelty at the edge of chaos (Stacey, 2000) and autopoesis; self-replication based on recurring patterns in chaos called fractals seen at every layer from micro- to mega- throughout the system (Wheatley, 1994; Maturana & Varela, 1998). Ashby's law contends that the part of the system with the most prolific repertoire of responses has most control over the system (Ashby, 1956). Human society and the communities in which health care functions can also be helpfully considered as complex adaptive systems, the second embedded within the first. Therefore, in complex systems terms the NHS is embedded in UK health care, itself embedded in UK society embedded in human society. Society is changing faster than the NHS, and there is a real sense in which the social structures of the NHS no longer replicate those emergent in society. The NHS is more hierarchical, observes many, more rigid, unchanging boundaries, is capable of limited stereotypical responses and fails to respect diversity (both cultural and in accepting individual behaviours) more like British society of the time of its inception. Its information-handling is also well behind that seen in sectors such as retail, travel and banking. Thus, the NHS and its institutions are not very faithful fractals of modern UK society and have the potential to be in conflict with it, evidence of which is seen by many of us in UK health care, being particularly evident within or around clinical micro-systems where the two interact. From the mystical tradition (Gergen, 2001) it has been claimed that:

> "The NHS is the last great religion of the UK. Everyone wishes it well and worships at its temples from time to time. The trouble is that the high priests are losing touch with the congregation."
>
> *(Neuberger, 1999)*

There are good social and complex systems reasons for fearing for the future of the NHS without major change to mirror social changes.

The definition of clinical micro-systems (Nelson *et al.*, 2002) places patients clearly outside their boundaries. Two considerations bring this definition into question. We aim for patient-centred care or co-creation of care with patients, yet this definition inserts the boundary exactly where the central focus of our interactions should be taking place. We also know that the costs of developments in medicine and health care are far out-stripping the capacity of all economies to pay for them. In order to sustain such developments in universal health care, most basic and low-tech health care will needed to be handed back to patients and their families, with quality in their self-care facilitated by professionals. In complexity terms we might think of clinical micro-systems as representing the fractal pattern at its smallest level, where the relationship between inter-personal interactions and effectiveness are manifest most clearly as co-creation of care. In this new model, patients and families are seen as *inside* clinical micro-systems, with professionals surrendering their dominance and patients their dependency. These changes mirror those in relationships and professional identity alluded to elsewhere in this chapter. During AI conversations we have shown that parents and patients can readily understand the complexity and limitations of health care services and delivery, and contribute to possibilities for a better future while professionals can enjoy empathising with families' specific needs and create relationships that are equal in the AI process. So far, we have focused on the nature of the delivery service. We wonder if the same kind of process can be used to co-create individual care.

To be successful, an emergent or autopoetic Managed Clinical Network would therefore need to replicate or at least reflect successful relationships and interactions from the social and micro-system levels. AI is an ideal way to recognise those interactions in practice and endorse them socially to be accepted as the benchmark for the current function of the MCN, and to ensure that they change as social expectations change. Certainly this MCN has emerged from pre-existing relationships with relatively little external effort. We shall see if it achieves a life of its own. If so, it may herald a different form of health care with greater flexibility and responsiveness, much looser "institutions" with negotiated rather than imposed boundaries between professionals and users. The interactions and relationships could be predicted to be much closer to those prevalent in society, possibly mirroring those of successful commercial, voluntary or social organisations. Management will be seen as facilitating the emergence of a collective vision among professionals and users and empowering its enactment, rather than dividing limited and shrinking resources among the competing problems with decisions based on critique or internal power in a vain attempt towards command and control.

■ References

Ashby, W. (1956) *An Introduction to Cybernetics.* London, Chapman & Hall.
Baker, A. & Wright, M. (2004) Using AI to initiate stakeholder interactions in health care, *AI Practitioner*, No. 2 (May), pp 31–33.
Boon, N.A. (2004) in *Health Services Management Centre*, Birmingham website.

Crib, A. & Bignold, S. (1999) Toward the reflexive medical school: the hidden curriculum and medical education research, *Studies In Higher Education*, No. 24, pp 195–209.

Department of Health (2004) *The National Service Framework For Children, Young People and Maternity Services*. HMSO.

Ferlie, E. & Pettigrew, A. (1996) Managing through networks: some issues and implications for the NHS. *British Journal of Management*, No. 7, pp. 81–99.

Gergen, K. (2001) *Social Construction In Context*. London, Sage Publications.

Institute of Medicine (2001). *Crossing The Quality Chasm: A New Health System For the 21st Century*. National Academy Press (USA).

King's Fund (2001) *A Patient-centred NHS?* King's Fund Briefing No.15, London, King's Fund.

Maddock, S. (2002) Modernisation work – new narratives, change strategies and people management in the public sector, *International Journal of Public Sector Management*, Vol. 15, No. 1, pp 13–44.

Magruder-Watkins, J. & Mohr, B. (2001) *Appreciative Inquiry*. San Francisco, Jossey-Bass/Pfeiffer.

Manificat, S., Dazord, A., Cochat, P., Morin, D., Plainguet, F. & Debray, D. (2003) Quality of life of children and adolescents after kidney or liver transplantation: child, parents and caregiver's points of view, *Paediatric Transplantation*, Vol.7, No.3, pp 228–35.

Mastroyannopoulou, K., Sclare, I., Baker, A. & Mowat, A (1998) Psychological effects of liver disease and transplantation, *European Journal of Paediatrics*, Vol. 157, No. 10, pp 856–60.

Maturana, H & Varela, F. (1998) *The Tree Of Knowledge*. New York, Shambhala Publications.

Menzies-Lyth, I. (1959) The functioning of social systems as a defence against anxiety: a report on a study of the nursing service of a general hospital, *Human Relations*, No. 13, pp. 95–121.

Nelson, E., Batalden, P., Huber, T., Mohr, J., Godrey, M., Headrick, L. & Wasson J. (2002) Micro-systems in healthcare: Part 1. High-performing front-line clinical units, *The Joint Commission on Quality Improvement*, Vol. 28, No. 9, pp. 72–493.

Neuberger, J. (1999) The NHS as a theological institution. *British Medical Journal*, No. 31915, pp. 88–89.

NHS Executive (2000) *Managed Clinical Networks*. London: NHS Executive, South East Regional Office.

Passmore, J. (2003) *Professional Standards Research: Appreciative Inquiry*. http://www.opm.co.uk/download/papers/appreciative_inquiry.doc.

Stacey, R., Griffin, D. & Shaw, P. (2000) *Complexity and Management: Fad or Radical Challenge?* New York, Routledge.

Surowecki, J. (2004) *The Wisdom of Crowds*. Little Brown Books, London.

Timmins, N. (2002) A final chance for return to health. *Financial Times*. 17/4/2004.http://specials.ft.com/budget2002/FT3NV7K50D.hmtl

Wheatley, M. (1994) *Leadership and the New Science: Learning about Organisations from an Orderly Universe*. San Francisco, CA: Berrett-Koehler.

Wright, M. & Baker, A. (2005) The effects of Appreciative Inquiry interviews on staff in the UK National Health Service. *International Journal of Healthcare Quality Assurance*, in press.

Evaluating the cancer services collaborative improvement partnership: an Appreciative Inquiry case study

Jill Turner and Jan Reed

■ Introduction

The use of Appreciative Inquiry as a routine approach to evaluate aspects of healthcare services is not yet widely established. However, this technique can provide rich qualitative learning about systems, processes and organisational change.

The Cancer Services Collaborative Improvement Partnership has adopted Appreciative Inquiry as one of several evaluation techniques in relation to its work with the English Cancer Networks to improve cancer services and to meet the requirements of the NHS Cancer Plan 2000.[1]

This case study describes the unique and innovative contribution made by Appreciative Inquiry to exploring the development of the Cancer Services Collaborative Improvement Partnership from a limited pilot programme through to full national coverage. This learning will inform its future development and will be shared with other similar national service improvement programmes.

■ Background to cancer services improvement

Cancer is a major healthcare challenge in the United Kingdom. One in three people will develop cancer and one in four will die of it.

Cancer services in England are organised into managed clinical networks comprising specialist cancer centres, and cancer units offering less complex care, in line with the recommendation of the Calman-Hine report (DoH, 1995). This report recommended that services should be reorganised to ensure that they are delivered by the most appropriate specialist, in the best location and at the appropriate time.

Managed clinical networks were developed as the most appropriate organisational model for planning and delivering cancer services. Each network embraces all the local health care organisations that provide these services, spanning primary, secondary and tertiary care; both NHS and independent sector providers and service commissioners. Serving local populations of between 750,000 to nearly three million people, networks also vary in terms of the range of services available locally, and their requirements to refer patients to other networks.

The first concerted attempts to improve cancer services in the NHS were to ensure greater standardisation and to improve patient outcomes included national guidance and screening programmes for breast and cervical cancer.

A national target was set in 1997 to reduce the death rate from cancer in people under 75 by at least 20% by 2010. Additional investment was also made to reduce waiting times and to update cancer services equipment.

Following the change of government in the UK in 1997, progress towards the devolution of political power in Scotland, Wales and Northern Ireland was accelerated with the accompanying differential approaches to health care services. Consequently, cancer services in the four UK countries are being developed according to different plans and timetables.

The English NHS Cancer Plan seeks to reduce waiting times at all stages of the patient's cancer journey. New targets were set in addition to the requirement that all patients with suspected cancer should be seen by a specialist within two weeks of referral by their General Practitioner. These were:

- A maximum one-month wait from urgent General Practitioner referral to treatment for children's and testicular cancers and acute leukaemia by 2001.
- A maximum one-month wait from diagnosis to treatment for patients with breast cancer by 2001.
- A maximum one-month wait from diagnosis to treatment for patients with any cancer by 2005.
- A maximum two-month wait from urgent General Practitioner referral to treatment for patients with breast cancer by 2002.
- A maximum two-month wait from urgent General Practitioner referral to treatment for patients with any cancer by 2005.

■ The Cancer Services Collaborative

The Cancer Services Collaborative (CSC) was established in England in response to concerns that cancer patient outcomes varied between geographic areas and social classes. In addition, relative survival rates in England

and Wales were generally lower than corresponding European and US averages (Coleman *et al.*, 1999, Berrino *et al.*, 1999, National Cancer Institute, 1998). Furthermore, waiting times following initial referral for a specialist opinion varied significantly between specialties (Spurgeon *et al.*, 2000); there was often poor communication and lack of systematic planning between professions and agencies, and patients reported poor experiences of care.

Subsequent to the launch of the Cancer Services Collaborative as a pilot programme, the NHS Cancer Plan for England was published in 2000. Seeking to address a range of problems associated with cancer services, and drawing on some of the early learning from the CSC, the Plan contained recommendations and targets covering prevention, screening, diagnosis, waiting times, treatment, workforce, research and development. This national cancer services strategy aims primarily to:

- Save more lives.
- Ensure that cancer patients receive the most appropriate and the best treatments, professional support and care.
- Invest in the cancer workforce, research and preparation for the genetics revolution, so that "the NHS never falls behind in cancer care again".

Several key challenges to be addressed for the future were identified:

- Better prevention.
- Action on health inequalities.
- Earlier detection.
- Faster diagnosis and treatment.
- Consistent, high quality services.
- Improved quality of life through better care.

The Plan was accompanied by significant additional investment for cancer services by 2003/04, which would be available in exchange for reforms and improvements across the entire system of cancer services. The Cancer Services Collaborative was regarded as the major means of achieving the Cancer Plan targets through its work to improve clinical systems and processes across the patient "journey" and across many boundaries, organisations and professions, via the medium of managed clinical networks.

The Cancer Services Collaborative was the first attempt to apply to the NHS the Collaborative Improvement Model, which had been developed by Dr Don Berwick at the Institute for Healthcare Improvement in Boston, USA. Berwick's model was underpinned by an improvement process based on many years of experience in improvement science (Langley *et al.*, 1996).

Berwick blended these principles with late twentieth century approaches to organisational development, and set them in the context of clinical team-driven improvements to health care services. In particular, the approach focussed on reducing avoidable waits and delays by adopting a system-wide perspective on the need for change and improvement.

During Phase 1 (1999–2001) of the Cancer Services Collaborative, nine pilot cancer networks were led and supported by the National Patients' Access Team (NPAT), which subsequently became part of the Modernisation Agency (MA); a Department of Health organisation that had been established to address the ongoing NHS difficulties of waiting lists and access problems. The CSC pilots worked together to improve cancer services from the patient's perspective, and collectively to develop the knowledge about how to create and to spread sustainable service improvements.

During Phase 2 (2001–2003) the national programme was duly extended to all thirty-four English cancer networks. A broader range of cancer and related services including gynaecology, urology, primary care and radiotherapy was included.

■ The Cancer Services Collaborative and evaluation

The Cancer Services Collaborative has consistently adopted a positive approach towards evaluation, knowledge management and related initiatives in order to avoid duplication of effort and waste of resources, and to accelerate the implementation of service improvements. Early work in Phase 1 included identifying and developing four main "change strategies" that were generic to all tumour services and, indeed, to other non cancer services.

1. Connect up the patient's journey.
2. Develop the team around the patient's journey.
3. Make the patient/carer experience central to every stage of the journey.
4. Ensure there is capacity to meet patient needs at every stage of the journey.

Cancer-specific work included the preparation of detailed guidance and CSC case studies for each tumour service and associated areas such as patient and carer involvement.

Evaluation initiatives have included an external quantitative evaluation of the impact of Phase 1 led by the Health Services Management Unit at the University of Birmingham, which focussed primarily on reductions in waiting times and cost data. Evaluation of specific qualitative aspects of the CSC and the Modernisation Agency's Booking Programme has also been undertaken by the Modernisation Agency's Research Into Practice Team. Examples include the factors that influence clinicians to become positively involved and the underlying features that support sustainable service improvement including strong clinical and managerial leadership and demonstrable benefits. To date the Cancer Services Collaborative evaluation has focussed primarily on qualitative dimensions such as:

- The structural organisation of the Cancer Services Collaborative at national and local levels.
- Establishing measurement and reporting systems.
- Factors determining the spread of improvement initiatives.
- Factors determining the sustainability of improvement initiatives.
- Quantification of improvement initiatives, especially reduction in waiting times, improved rates of booking for services and the management of patient care by multi-disciplinary teams.

With the exception of work to evaluate patient and carer experience, relatively little attention has been given by the Cancer Services Collaborative to exploring other qualitative dimensions of the programme, particularly with the objective of learning from the experience and perceptions of programme participants; managers and clinicians. Aspects of the CSC's experience, which may be relevant to similar large scale service improvement initiatives include developing a national programme, working with innovators, extending the programme across the entire NHS, and embedding the improvement activity into daily working practices. These generic dimensions are anticipated to be of relevance to other national programmes, particularly as they develop from centrally-led initiatives to locally-focussed and locally-led mainstream activity.

■ The Cancer Services Collaborative and Appreciative Inquiry

The Cancer Services Collaborative consciously adopted Appreciative Inquiry as a different approach to exploring the qualitative dimensions of its work, in particular its development and progress from a small pilot programme to a fully national initiative. Appreciative Inquiry offered a new perspective to evaluation of CSC work with its focus on the individual experiences and perceptions of staff members. Through its encouragement to explore the successful dimensions of their contribution and valuing their work, it was hoped that programme participants would look forward and plan positively to take account of these features in their future work. Likewise, the programme could develop its overall learning and understanding of successful approaches to change management.

The Cancer Services Collaborative Improvement Partnership Evaluation Steering Group worked with Professor Jan Reed, from the Centre for the Care of Older People, University of Northumbria, and used the Appreciative Inquiry approach in order to evaluate the transition from CSC Phase 1 to 2 (pilot to full national roll-out) and the accompanying issues surrounding longer-term sustainability into Phase 3. An acknowledged expert in this field, Professor Reed devised a series of questions that were designed to explore the background to the transition from the Appreciative Inquiry perspective.

■ Questions and interviews

The questions that were formulated are itemised below, and were sent to respondents before a telephone interview was conducted in order to allow the respondent to think about the issues that would be covered in the interview. While this strategy meant that responses would be less spontaneous, it was felt that the questions did need some thought if replies were to be comprehensive. In addition, the study was carried out in a collaborative manner, and so openness about the interview agenda was necessary to ensure that this was maintained, and that respondents felt fully aware of the questions that would be asked, and would feel able to suggest areas or topics of their own.

The questions were not set into a rigid schedule, and the interviews had the capacity to involve a lot of discussion with questions, which explored points further.

Questions

- Looking back over the life of the project, how do you think it has developed? What stories do people tell about the project and its achievements?

- Are there any key events or defining moments in the history of the project, where it all started to come together? What happened? Who was there? What made it special? What did you and your team do? How? What was different? What remained the same?

- What pleased you about your part in the process? What do you value about your situation, which enabled you to behave in the way that you did? How do you think things have changed over the life-span of the CSCIP?

- Suppose one night a miracle occurred and everything is in place to make the service sustainable and able to respond to future challenges. How would you know? What would be the same? What would better for you? What would be happening?

- What have you learned about creating a responsive and flexible service that you will take forward into the future? What advice would you give others trying to develop a service from where yours started to where it is today?

Selection of interviewees

In order to secure a wide focus for the Appreciate Inquiry project, the Project Team agreed that interviewees should be selected according to the following principles:

- Mix of Phases 1, 2 and 3 personnel.
- Mix of professional staff e.g. medical, nursing, managerial and other clinical.
- Mix of staff with differing levels of seniority within the programme ranging from national lead roles through to network and Trust level personnel.
- Mix of geographic spread across England.
- Mix of the tumour and cross tumour work streams.
- Inclusive of known "cynics"/"converts" and "champions".

Care was also taken where possible to avoid selecting staff who had been interviewed previously for other CSC research and evaluation work.

Recruitment of respondents

From a list of twenty-five potential respondents supplied by the Appreciative Inquiry Evaluation Steering Group, the researcher contacted twenty-one to invite them to participate. Four from the list were not approached, as they had primarily clinical roles, rather than strategic leadership responsibilities. Of the twenty-one contacted, twenty agreed to take part in a telephone interview – the remaining person could not be traced as she had changed jobs. All those agreeing to take part were sent a copy of the Appreciative Inquiry questions, a project information sheet and a consent form, stating that the interviews would remain confidential and the data would be anonymised. Appointments were then made to carry out the interviews. This proved to be a difficult process, as work responsibilities meant that approximately 50% of interviews had to be cancelled and re-arranged because of competing priorities – particularly the case for respondents who also had clinical responsibilities. Eighteen people finally took part in interviews, the remaining two participants were not able to set interview dates within the timescale of the evaluation.

■ The analysis and findings

The major themes to emerge from the Appreciative Inquiry interviews are set out below in chronological sequence of the Cancer Services Collaborative's programme phases.

It is now intended to share widely both the report and the analysis of the findings with other NHS service improvement programmes.

Phase I: piloting change

Character

All respondents reported that Phase 1 had been regarded as a "special" stage, given a high profile and reported on and discussed throughout the wider community of cancer care services, and indeed in health care generally. Such a profile gave the pilot phase a "buzz" as several respondents put it, and for those working in the pilot projects, this had been energising and motivating. One respondent described her involvement as:

> "The most exciting thing I've ever done at work! We all felt that we'd been given the scope to really do things the way we wanted to."

For those involved in the pilot work, the practice changes had not been imposed on them, but had developed from their past experience and thinking – it was an opportunity to put long-held ideals and innovations into practice:

> "We'd been thinking along those lines for a long time. We'd been talking about what we could do or try out if we got the chance, and being a pilot was the chance we were waiting for."

Focus and content

For those outside the pilot projects, the development of the Cancer Services Collaborative could be demoralising, as attention was not paid to what they were doing. As one respondent put it:

> "The pilots were seen as the elite, and everyone else felt that they were being unfairly expected to reach their standards."

This thinking was not necessarily a consequence of the Collaborative's strategy, but was described by one respondent as a hangover from "old" NHS culture:

> "The NHS is used to top-down change, so there's sometimes an in-built suspicion of change – at first every change is seen as a top-down imposition, even if it's not. It will take a long time to change that."

The establishment of the Cancer Services Collaborative involved significant new learning for the NHS covering aspects such as setting up a nation-wide change programme, training staff in improvement methodologies and capturing the learning. While the pilots had been designed as opportunities to tease-out the practical implications of changing practice in a very focussed way in a few services, this had been misinterpreted by some as a lack of acknowledgement of the problems facing other services and different contexts:

> "There was a feeling that we'd all be expected to do the same as them – that we'd all have to be clones and follow the pilots to the letter, even if we were in very different circumstances."

Roles, skills and processes

The skills that people reported developing if they were involved in a pilot were mainly about negotiating with people outside the team – they did not report a need to motivate teams, as they were already enthusiastic and committed. Others, however, were suspicious of the proposed changes, and could be either very cynical or hostile and obstructive. This required well-developed skills in diplomacy to manage:

> "I knew that there were some people who just thought it was just another gimmick – that nothing would really change, and they could go on with things the way they always had been, once the fuss had died down. I had to break it to them that this was a real change, but I had to do it so that they wouldn't get hostile."

A key message that emerged from the Appreciative Inquiry evaluation was that if preparatory discussions were not held, then the pilots could face huge problems, with others in the system sabotaging or not helping. The pilot leaders, then, needed to find out who to approach to gain their support, and how it would be best to approach them:

> "If you understand where people are coming from, then you can really tackle them with those things in mind – you know what their anxieties are likely to be, and what their concerns are, so you can really make your case relevant to them."

While some participants described a degree of discomfort with having to develop strategies to "sell' their pilot, a belief that what they were selling was worthwhile was a strong motivator:

> "I sometimes feel like I'm selling double glazing, and you can see them thinking "Oh no, it's the cancer people again!" but I really do think that this is worth doing, and that keeps me going, and I think they respect that, and it wins them over in the end."

This approach was not uniformly successful, for example in lung services there was a feeling that cancer patients were unfairly prioritised above other patients with equally life threatening conditions, but for whom there was greater potential for survival if treatment was available.

Phase 2: spreading change

Character

The lessons from Phase I were rolled-out across England in a centrally-led programme with strong co-ordination and leadership. However, the perception of top-down change created a barrier to adoption in some areas:

> "It took a while to convince people that they didn't have to adopt recommendations like robots, regardless of their particular context."

At times, project leaders found themselves in difficult positions when asked to implement ideas that others had developed:

> "I felt that some of the proposed changes would not work in my area – they had been developed in very different circumstances, so I was reserving my judgement on whether they would work."

"Conversion" could be a gradual process or it could be quite sudden. Whatever the trajectory, people reported that opportunities to discuss the Collaborative, at conferences and workshops were very useful. In particular, the process of becoming familiar with the methodology of change was very useful. Learning about how to guide people through process mapping, for example, made service development "come alive" for them.

In turn, when programme leaders sought to involve and enthuse practitioners and others involved in service delivery, they found that key points in the process often came at workshop or meetings, particularly when they centred around process mapping. This often resulted in service providers and delivers "seeing things with fresh eyes", looking at taken-for-granted processes and re-thinking them quite radically.

Roles, skills and processes

The skills that were necessary in Phase 2 were different from Phase I, and related primarily to motivating a wide range of people, with different attitudes to change in general, and the Cancer Services Collaborative in particular. In Phase I the teams were committed and enthused and the skills were mainly about negotiating with key stakeholders outside the teams. However, in Phase 2 more motivating work was required to encourage others to take part. The Plan-Do-Study-Act improvement methodology helped, as identified above, as a tool to change people's ideas. The use of this methodology, however, required people to have facilitator skills and to be sensitive to participants' anxieties and concerns:

> "You can't go in there and insist that people do what you want. They might do it, but it would only be to keep you happy. If you want them to really take it on board then you need to win their hearts as well."

That sometimes meant being aware of and sensitive to the group's hidden agendas:

> "If they're worried that their heads are on the block, or that they are being forced to do something they don't want to do, then you have to get over that. I do it by being as non-threatening as possible, and making sure that everyone has their say, so that they feel that its not a one-way thing – you must do this."

The Cancer Services Collaborative staff valued the credibility derived from the training they received in the improvement methodology. Of equal, if not greater importance was training in the interpersonal skills necessary to achieve successful changes in the way of working at local level. Expertise in managing the "human dimensions of change" and facilitation was cited frequently as of critical value for securing support, for motivating and for targeting potential resistors.

Meeting with individuals also required interpersonal and motivational skills, and again, as in Phase 1, a thorough understanding of structures, contexts and interpersonal dynamics:

> "I had to go and see one consultant, famous for being difficult, who didn't like anything that challenged the status quo, and I really prepared carefully for that, finding out what were the key issues. So I could go in and say, "Look, I know that these are your problems, and if we work together we can solve them." Things went really smoothly after that – I think there was an idea that the Cancer Services Collaborative would make life more difficult, not easier, and that we would be arrogant and dismiss problems."

Some participants found themselves in a difficult position, caught between the complaints of practitioners and the requirements of the CSC roll-out process. This could demand sophisticated relationship management skills:

> "Sometimes I've found myself in the position of a go-between – the people on the ground will be digging their heels in, often for quite legitimate reasons, while the Cancer Services Collaborative are saying "What's going on there? Why aren't you getting on with it?" I have to make sure that the messages I give to both parties don't make things worse, so I sometimes have to be very tactful."

Managing the paradox of being open and democratic, while at the same time being quite focused on achieving pre-determined targets called for a range of different strategies and skills:

> "Sometimes, when I've been piggy in the middle, I have to use my local knowledge to decide what would be the most effective strategy. I support the overall CSC goals, but if I think we'll get more progress by backing-off a bit, then I'll do that. What matters is getting a result in the long run."

Focus and content

It was important not to dismiss the previous experience and achievements of front- line staff when extending the programme. Staff needed to feel that their contribution was valued alongside the persistent help, support and guidance that accompanied the Cancer Services Collaborative in its national roll-out phase across the major cancer services.

The support provided for local clinical teams by trained project staff was highly valued, and some concerns were expressed about the sustainability of the work after the central initiative ceased.

The importance of frequent and effective communications between all parties was also emphasised repeatedly – inclusivity was crucial.

The overall importance and value of the goal of improving cancer services was a motivating and sustaining factor, particularly through challenging situations, although programme staff frequently experienced conflict in their roles between a centrally-led (top-down) initiative and front-line staff with a range of local challenges and circumstances.

Phase 3

Character

This phase highlighted devolution to local leadership and initiatives, and many respondents commented that people were much happier with this. One respondent, for example stated:

> "I think people felt that they were given the opportunity to get local issues
> sorted out, setting their own priorities and goals, rather than just fit into a
> national programme."

Another commented on the change in enthusiasm at the start of Phase 3:

> "Instead of just plodding through a set of objectives that they didn't feel part of,
> they were keen to get going addressing the problems that they saw in their patch."

Focus and content

Phase 3 was characterised by an increased sense of ownership among participants. This did not mean, however, that Phase 2 had been of no value – respondents commented on the value of the Phase 2 activity:

> "To be honest, I don't think we could have done Phase 3 without the
> experience of Phase 2 – it was difficult, but I also think it was essential."

The value of Phase 2 lay in the way it had prepared the foundations for Phase 3. This happened in several ways, including building-up relationships and networks. Phase 2 had also helped people to develop networks outside their locality, which had been important for Phase 3:

> "People feel that they can just phone up someone that they got to know
> through the CSC and they can pick their brains, knowing that it's safe and it
> won't involve any internal politics."

Respondents reported that one of the key features of Phase 3 had been a wider sense of community between people involved in developing cancer services – a community which had taken shape in earlier phases of the Collaborative, but was now maturing:

> "You meet people, and you find that they all know each other, and what
> they're up to. They might not talk to each other very often, but you feel that
> they have a strong sense of community."

A point made by many respondents was that, whether Cancer Services Collaborative participants were working in harmony or were in disagreement, the factor that had bound them together was their concern for the patient, for doing the best they could to make services better. The touchstone of the patient could be used as a lever for change:

> "When somebody's getting entrenched, and sometimes defensive, and you
> think things are getting completely stuck, going back to the patient really gets
> it going again. Because whatever people's personal axes to grind are, that's the
> bottom-line for everybody. And you get people saying, well the patient's
> going to suffer if I don't get my way, but when they have to justify their
> argument, then they soon back-track."

Roles, skills and processes

In Phase 3 the skills needed were those which would firstly maintain change and secondly extend it. Maintaining change meant that people had to be encouraged to keep going – to see that changing processes was not just a one-off exercise:

> "You can tell that some people are thinking "Oh well, that's that done", as if it were just something where they could tick a box and forget about it, but that's not it, they need to be going back to it, and reviewing it and seeing if it's still working."

The notion of change maintenance was one which some respondents described as new to the NHS where change had often been episodic, and where changes were quietly reversed once attention had moved on:

> "In the past you did something because other people told you to, and so when they moved on to other things, you were off the hook and you just let things go back to where they were."

Getting people to maintain change therefore meant that they had to be encouraged to own and have a stake in change:

> "You've got to say to them "This is yours. You've done it because you believed in it." They've got to own it rather than feel it's been forced on them, and as soon as the heat dies down they can go back to what they did before."

Balancing the dynamics of centrally-developed change with local issues required sensitivity and understanding of local contexts:

> "You've got to make the links between principles of change and local drivers – you've got to be able to say "Look at that clinic you've changed – it fits in exactly with what the programme is trying to do." So that you can give them examples of the way it fits."

Interviewees also used strategies like "burning bridges" to consolidate change:

> "Sometimes people spend a lot of time dithering, wanting to keep a foot in both camps, so they can go back if it doesn't work out. Sometimes you have to give them a push, get them to make a decisive move, so you might encourage them to make a change they can't go back on, or declare a policy publicly so they've burnt their bridges and they can't go back. Otherwise they'd be dithering forever."

Sometimes interviewees had found other ways to consolidate change, by encouraging people to take "next steps" – in other words getting them to build on what they had already achieved:

> "You need to look back at what they've done and pick out their achievements, and tell them what they've done, because sometimes they don't realise it themselves. Then you can say "Well, you've done this, why not take it a little bit further." Then they can see that they can do it, and would be silly not to."

Getting people to engage in constant development, however, involved making sure that they felt confident about what they had already done:

> "You've got to say to them "Look – this is what you've achieved." and show them the proof. It's a bit like coaching, really – they don't believe they can do it until you show them."

Ultimately, however, interviewees wanted to move from the coaching role to a more distant role, which gave services more independence:

> "I can't always be there holding their hands – they've got to go off and do it themselves. They need to set-up their own processes for monitoring what they are doing now and planning what they are doing in the future."

This future planning could also be facilitated by encouraging staff to make connections with other developments:

> "Sometimes you can say "Well that would fit in with what so-and-so is doing over there, so you could work together." Sometimes it's not even a cancer-related service – maybe something about central services, or an Ambulance Trust, but if they can make connections it helps to consolidate the changes by tying them to wider developments."

There was another set of minefields to be negotiated, however. Much as the pilot projects had been regarded with some suspicion across cancer services in Phases 1 and 2, cancer services were sometimes regarded with suspicion by other services within and outside the NHS:

> "People say 'Well, why should cancer services get all the resources and the kudos? We're just as important." And they've got a point – there are many other health problems around. But you've got to be an ambassador and say this is what CSC have done, and they want to share it with you. You've got to be positive about their comments and acknowledge that they've been doing some good things too, without the fanfare."

Learning about roles and processes for change

Overall, involvement in the Cancer Services Collaborative had taken people outside traditional NHS structures and roles. This process could be difficult and/or liberating. For some there was a hostility to the Collaborative which meant that they had to develop different techniques for facilitating change – traditional line management strategies did not work, not only because they were not in a line management position, but because to do so would have gone against the spirit of the collaboration:

> "Sometimes I get a bit frustrated, because I just think that if I had more authority, they would just have to get on with it, but we're trying to do things differently. People have to want to do things differently, not just because they've been told to."

The respondents, therefore, described their role as facilitative, rather than didactic and different from previous change strategies, which some had found difficult:

> "In the NHS people expect you to storm and shout, and tell people what to do, and the Modernisation Agency was expected to carry on the tradition. When I stood up and didn't do this, they were quite taken aback – they were spoiling for a fight and I wasn't giving them one. If anything I was agreeing with them. They were completely thrown by that."

Respondents had to develop alternative roles and images, being careful to be non-judgemental and discreet. Two central roles had been that of "coach" within projects, and "ambassadors" outside. As coaches, they had learned to be facilitating rather than didactic, and to understand how to motivate people and to sustain that motivation. An important part of this was helping people to collect and analyse data that would show them what difference they were making:

> "Sometimes they don't realise that there is evidence of change there, if they collect it properly. They need to set up their own systems for auditing and evaluating. Central statistics won't always tell them what they need to know."

Even when the information was there, people often had to be encouraged to learn from it, in a non-threatening way:

> "A lot of the time they're so used to being told they're doing it wrong, that when you praise them they're a bit taken aback – they're not sure if it's a trick."

Tools and resources for developing the cancer services collaborative

Interviewees named a number of "tools" or resources that they had used or developed over time. These included:

Interpersonal skills – understanding where people were coming from and being able to respond to these agendas and personal styles:

> "Sometimes you get some really aggressive and defensive people, and you've got to be able to roll with the punches, and establish a working relationship that is going to get you all where you want to go, which is providing better services."

Communication Styles – open and transparent, with no hidden agendas:

> "You've got to be able to say "I don't know." or "I got that wrong." If you're not open, and able to let your defences down, then you can't expect anyone else to be, and if you all worry about what you look like, then you're so busy covering-up and watching your back that nothing will move on."

The ability to be open required a high degree of self-confidence and such openness could leave people vulnerable:

> "The first time you say "I don't know." everything goes quiet and you think "They think I'm incompetent." So you got to be able to deal with that."

Process mapping and the use of service improvement tools – this was effective in making people re-think existing practices and processes in a way, which was logical and factual:

> "People get very heated and want to defend their position come what may, but if you take them through a process mapping exercise, then they are presented with facts in a safe way, not as a challenge, but to get the debate on a more even keel, getting people off their soapboxes."

Turning points

Through using these tools and resources, interviewees felt that they had contributed to the change process, even though it may have been a slow and partial process. All had encountered resistance, either within projects or from outside, but all had identified "turning points" or instances where they had felt that this resistance was shifting Sometimes this came when people who had previously been hostile or cynical about the work admitted that it had value.

More subtle signs that the Programme was becoming part of everyday practices had also been identified:

> "It's not always something huge. It might be that you notice that people are using the language in everyday conversation, and no-one comments on it. Or when people are using the methodology as a matter of routine – it's taken for granted."

These turning points are much more subtle than any formal evaluation of progress, which may tend to produce the answers that people want to hear. They are more immediate than looking at outcomes of care, which, although these may be the ultimate goal, are somewhat distant. Being able to spot them, however, is dependent on close and sustained working, sophisticated interpersonal awareness, and the ability to build constraint-free collaborative relationships.

Satisfactions

There were many satisfactions reported by interviewees. Among the most important, and most emphasised were:

Empowerment of staff

Several interviewees commented on the empowering effects of the process of change – when traditions and customs were challenged, existing hierarchies could be too. This opened up the possibility that everyone could instigate and own change, rather than just follow top-down directions. One interviewee gave an example of a ward clerk who had re-organised appointment systems to make them more efficient and user-friendly. This had made the ward clerk feel valued and acknowledged and had made others think about what they could do.

When services become patient-centred

Linked to the empowerment of staff was the empowerment of patients, as services became more patient-centred. This could be demonstrated through the changes made, which had the patients' preferences and needs at the centre, or in the processes of deciding on change, where the patient perspective was the starting point for change.

When people work across barriers

Another satisfaction identified was the way in which barriers between services began to break down. People would work in partnership with other services and sectors, holding meetings and discussions and jointly planning initiatives. This could be formal, as groups were constituted or as committees that were given authority to make decisions. It could also be informal, as people across services got to know each other and consulted each other, asking advice and getting information and ideas from each other.

Lessons

When asked, interviewees identified the following key lessons:

Be inclusive – for changes to be successful, as many stakeholders as possible need to be involved, from junior to senior staff and across service boundaries. Inclusion might need to be staged and strategically managed, but it needed to be comprehensive, as those not included could become resistant to the changes, feeling marginalised and unvalued.

Be persistent and committed – change was a slow process, and was not always linear – there were steps forward but also steps back in the process. Expecting quick and easy progress was unrealistic, and change had to be carefully prepared for. This included doing "homework" finding out about the people and policies in the service, and developing an understanding of the issues they faced.

Be credible – part of the process of working with others was "testing-out" the interviewees' knowledge and experience. While some had worked in the organisations before, and had built-up some credibility, others were new to the organisation, and had to establish their credentials. This involved disclosing past work, knowledge, training and experience, before interviewees felt that they would be taken seriously and listened to.

Be positive yet realistic – being too sweeping or grandiose in ambition was a pitfall to be avoided. Setting over-ambitious goals built failure into the system, and created disillusionment and disappointment. Medium or small-scale goals, which were achievable, were a more effective way to enthuse staff, and if they fitted in to a longer-term strategy were useful markers of progress.

■ Conclusions

The Health Service has a history of top-down initiatives implemented through hierarchical systems and so any attempt to change practice and service delivery has to contend with reluctance from staff, based on suspicion and hostility. This is not universal, as some staff are enthusiastic for change, but significant numbers will have an understandable antipathy to what may be simply the latest in a series of change programmes.

Where the Cancer Services Collaborative initiative succeeded then, was in replacing old-fashioned didactic change strategies with a more inclusive, collaborative approach, in which all stakeholders felt valued and appreciated.

The "glue" that held this diverse group together was the patient – concern for patient welfare was the touchstone for change, the measure of success and the decider of goals. While cancer may be a particularly feared illness, which touches many lives, this concern for the patient offers the potential for change to be rolled-out to other services and areas of care.

In conclusion, the Appreciative Inquiry approach to evaluating the development of the Cancer Services Collaborative Improvement Partnership provided rich and detailed insight into the actual experience, thoughts and reactions of the participants and their colleagues working in the cancer networks.

The unique Appreciative Inquiry focus on positive dimensions and experiences enabled the interviewees to explore their feelings and build on their experiences in making recommendations for future similar initiatives. Building on approaches that are known to work, alongside personal successes and values, is a demonstrably successful technique which could be applied more widely across aspects of health care development.

■ References

Berrino, R., Capocaccia, J., Esteve, G., Gatta, G., Hakulinen, T., Micheli, A., Sant, M. & Verdecchia, A. (1999) *Survival Of Cancer Patients In Europe: The Eurocare Study: II*, Scientific Publication No. 151, IARC, Lyon.

Coleman, M., Babb, P., Damiecki, P., Grosclaude, P., Honjo, S., Jones, J., Knerer, G., Pitard, A., Quinn, M., Sloggett, A. & De Stavola, B. (1999) *Cancer Survival Trends In England and Wales: 1971–1995*, London, HMSO.

Department of Health (2000) *NHS Cancer Plan*, London, HMSO.

Department of Health (1995) *A Policy Framework For Commissioning Cancer Services* (Calman-Hine report), London, HMSO.

Langley, G., Nolan, K., Nolan, T., Norman, C. & Provost, L. (1996) *The Improvement Guide*, San Francisco, Jossey-Bass.

National Cancer Institute (1998) *SEER Stat-Cancer Incident Public Use Database: 1973–95*, Release 1.1, Bethesda, MD, USA.

Spurgeon, P., Barwell, F. & Kerr, W. (2000) Waiting times for cancer patients in England after general practitioner referrals: retrospective national survey, *British Medical Journal*, No. 320, pp. 838–839.

6 Appreciative Inquiry in the context of the Royal College of Nursing Clinical Leadership Programme

Hazel Mackenzie and Theresa Douglas

■ Introduction

The purpose of this chapter is to present a case study outlining the use of Appreciative Inquiry in the context of the Royal College of Nursing Clinical Leadership Programme (RCN CLP). The details of the Programme will be presented in the first section, along with a description of the background to this successful leadership development programme. Some time will also be spent looking at the structure of the programme and the challenges which this presents.

Having set the context, the rationale for selecting Appreciative Inquiry will be presented and the design described. The outcomes from the application of Appreciative Inquiry to the evaluation of the Programme in Scotland and the development of the team of Local Facilitators is discussed and followed by some concluding remarks.

■ Case study context: background

The RCN Clinical Leadership Programme is an 18-month programme that supports the development of clinical leaders within the context of their day-to-day practice, their organisational climate and the policy agenda. The aim is to enable them to improve their leadership capability; to lead their teams in providing clinical care that is patient-centred and evidence-based, thereby promoting improvements in the quality of patient care.

The RCN Ward Nursing Leadership Project (Cunningham & Kitson, 1997) was the starting-point. Although patients and their families should be able to expect high standards of care, delivered by kind and understanding professional nurses, many realised this did not always happen. The Ward

Nursing Leadership Project sought to identify why good care was not being delivered and then to explore ways to improve.

This initial Project ran from November, 1994 through to October, 1997 – led by the RCN and funded by a charitable trust. It was clear from existing research the pivotal role of the ward sister in determining the quality of care delivered within the ward. Good leaders produced good care and poor leaders produced poor care. The RCN Ward Leadership Project focused on the ward leader, the senior nurse, and their leadership qualities. The Project aimed to promote better practice by identifying the skills needed by ward leaders to make them more effective, then demonstrating how those skills could then be transferred to nurses and patients.

One of the strongest messages to emerge was that, although employers can influence the quality of patient care, it is the qualities of individual nurses which have a more direct effect on the way patients are looked after. Five major themes emerged from the qualitative data. The themes illustrated the areas where participants needed to develop their skills in order to become patient-centred clinical leaders. Figure 6.1 summarises these key skills.

---

1. **Learning to manage self**
   The ability of ward leaders to learn the skills of self-management was crucial for all the nurses. Ward leaders reported that they became self-aware, less defensive, open to criticism, and more focused on delivering and improving the quality of care patients receive.

2. **Patient focus**
   New techniques were developed by ward leaders to enable them not only to monitor the development of their team, but also to ensure that the team was focused on needs of patients. Observation of care and patient stories enable nurses to explore how they delivered care to patients. This process of observation helped many nurses to recognise the shortcomings in their delivery of patient care.

3. **Political awareness**
   Political awareness skills developed as the ward leaders recognised the importance of being able to influence key stakeholders within their Trusts, so that resources could be used to promote improvements to patient care.

4. **Effective relationships**
   The need to influence their team of nurses and build relationships with other disciplines was also common to all the nurses who participated in the Project. These skills enabled ward leaders to develop staff in a way that directly influenced the delivery of patient care.

5. **Networking**
   Networking was also key in the ward leaders' development. The networks they developed were important – providing support and introducing the ward leaders to new ideas.

Figure 6.1 RCN clinical leadership framework

The RCN CLP consists of a number of interventions aimed at developing clinical leaders' capabilities around the areas highlighted in the framework. Research and evaluations of the Programme (Cunningham and Kitson, 2000a; Cunningham and Kitson, 2000b; Cunningham *et al.*, 2002; Mackenzie and Cunningham, 2002) and personal accounts (Carlowe and Cole, 1997; Hambridge, 1997; Black, 2000; Simons, 2003a; Simons, 2003b; Simons, 2003c; Govier, 2004) repeatedly indicate that the Programme supports clinical leaders to develop their skills in the areas highlighted in the framework and, although the framework emerged from research with ward leaders, the RCN CLP that has evolved is suitable for clinical leaders in any setting.

What started as an action research project involving four NHS Trusts in England is now an international initiative. The RCN Clinical Leadership Programme is now running across England, Wales and Scotland, Belgium, Switzerland and the first pilot in Australia has just been completed. Participants on the Programme come from a variety of clinical backgrounds, including hospital nurses, community nurses, doctors, and allied health professionals.

■ The drive for effective leadership

Government strategy for modernising the NHS in the UK has leadership development at the very heart of it. The importance of the issue is evident in the plethora of literature on the topic and the frequency with which policy documents call for effective leadership at every level of the NHS (DoH, 1999; DoH, 2000; SE, 2000; SE, 2001; SE, 2003). The Scottish Executive Health Department (SEHD) Framework for Leadership Development in NHS Scotland (Draft) (2004), identifies clinical leadership as one of the key priorities for leadership development and sets out some ambitious targets and timescales for NHS Boards.

In the literature, Goodwin (2000) states that the study of leadership generally has been prolific in recent years with 3,000 studies being published in 1974 rising to over 7,000 in 1990. A similar trend can be seen in the number of articles relating to leadership in the NHS. What is clear in the literature is that there is a shift away from focussing on "management" of the NHS and towards "leadership" in the NHS. Although leadership and management are both important, Bennis and Nanus identify a profound difference between the two, stating that:

> "Managers are people who do things right and leaders are people who do the right things"

> *(Bennis & Nanus, 1985)*

Trofino (1995) argues that the present healthcare context requires leaders who develop people committed to action, convert followers into an empowered workforce and transform leaders into change agents. Several writers suggest that a shift in leadership away from command-and-control styles and towards more transformational and facilitative styles is what is required in the NHS. In this paradigm leadership is defined as:

> "The art of mobilising others to want to struggle for shared aspirations"
>
> *(Kouzes & Posner, 1997)*

The literature in relation to leadership in the NHS is also notable in the extent to which the link between high-quality leadership and high-quality patient care is increasingly emphasised. The Scottish Executive boldly states that:

> "Improving the health of Scotland and reforming how healthcare is delivered depends on effective leadership at all levels of NHS Scotland"
>
> *(Scottish Executive, 2004)*

While there are a number of articles about the style of leadership required and the impact of leadership on the quality of care, there is comparatively little attention focussed on how to develop leadership potential in the NHS. It is therefore perhaps unremarkable that a recent major study (Alimo-Metcalfe and Alban-Metcalfe, 2003) of public sector mangers highlights some serious concerns about the quality of leadership in the NHS, suggesting that there is some way to go in realising the vision of transformational leadership.

■ The RCN Clinical Leadership Programme in Scotland

The RCN CLP is now the largest international clinical leadership development programme available in the UK which focuses on the development of transformational leadership behaviours.

A Local Facilitator is appointed by the participating NHS organisations to deliver the Programme and to support the participants. The Local Facilitator is therefore key to the success of the RCN Clinical Leadership Programme objectives being met and the impact on individuals, organisations and patients being articulated and disseminated, both locally and nationally. In this way the Programme informs and delivers the policy agenda.

As a "virtual team" this disparate group of highly skilled and motivated individuals work together collaboratively with their continuing development and support provided by the Scottish RCN Clinical Leadership Team.

■ Strengths and challenges

One of the key strengths of the Programme is that the Local Facilitator is employed by the NHS organisations. The role of the RCN Clinical Leadership Team is to support and develop the Local Facilitators through residential learning communities, coaching, Action Learning, workshops and continuing development days. In addition, the RCN Clinical Leadership Team delivers elements of the Programme with Local Facilitators to provide an opportunity to feedback on facilitation skills. In this way the Local Facilitators are simultaneously participants on, and facilitators of, the Programme. Furthermore, the expertise of the Local Facilitator is developed and retained as a resource within the local organisation.

While this model of working is a key strength, it also presents inherent challenges associated with working effectively in a virtual team where colleagues are geographically dispersed and employed by a range of organisations with varying cultures, needs and priorities. In addition, it is likely that the individuals' expectations of themselves within a new role, of their new colleagues and of the team will be diverse. It follows that the challenge for the RCN Clinical Leadership Team is to build a cohesive team culture with shared values and clear ways of working while being cognisant of the potential conflicts which may exist.

■ Rationale

There is a growing body of literature which focuses on Appreciative Inquiry as both a philosophical approach to, and a process of, organisational change and development. In addition Appreciative Inquiry has more recently been considered as an approach to coaching. (Zeus and Skiffington, 2002). Appreciative Inquiry is based on the work of David Cooperrider (Cooperrider and Barrett, 1990) who purports that how we think about and talk about our organisations influences how we work in them. Cooperrider believes that if we conceive of organisations as "problems to be solved" we end up in an endless cycle of problem-definition and problem-solution. This, in turn, saps energy for productive change. However, if we choose to see our organisations as "miracles to be appreciated" then we begin to focus on what is going well and we can intentionally amplify those positive factors. This in turn creates positive energy and the possibility for lasting change. (Goldberg, 2001)

Whitney (1998) provides a useful summary of the principles underpinning Appreciative Inquiry as follows:

- **The constructionist principle**: organisations are invented, enacted and maintained through processes of social interaction, and as a result are changed in the same manner.

- **The poetic principle**: organisations move in the direction of what is studied and what is talked about. They are guided by socially-created and ever-changing practices, not by unchangeable iron laws.

- **The anticipatory principle**: the stories told about an organisation's future are the best determinants of that future. Images, whether explicitly described or implicitly carried by organisation stakeholders, command great power over the future.

- **The simultaneity principle**: Organisation Development (OD) has historically been thought of as a long-term process involving step-by-step diagnosis, feedback, action planning and implementation. Appreciative Inquiry assumes, invites and evokes the simultaneity of learning and change.

- **The positive principle**: organisations can grow, develop and evolve by focussing on what gives life.

The rationale for selecting Appreciative Inquiry was based on the context of the work that is the RCN CLP and the particular task in hand. The task was to evaluate the first year of running the Programme across Scotland and to reflect on where we were as a virtual team of facilitators and how we needed to move forward. The principles underpinning Appreciative Inquiry sat well with the beliefs and values on which our work is based:

- Effective leaders provide high quality patient/client care.
- All health and social care practitioners require leadership skills.
- It is possible for individuals to develop their leadership capabilities.
- Potential is best developed in a culture of high support and high challenge.
- Participants bring rich and varied experience to the Programmes. The strengths of such diversity are best recognised, valued and mobilised through person-centred, experiential approaches to learning.
- Change, as well as being exciting and stimulating, can be a difficult and painful process.
- Effective leaders are able to influence local and national policy agendas and respond creatively to rapid and frequent change.

- For leadership initiatives to be successful they need to be supported at all levels of the organisation.

In summary, the principles that underpin our work on the RCN CLP focus around leadership as a process of development and change and in this way they fit well with the view of Appreciative Inquiry as a process for positive change (Cooperrider *et al.*, 1999). While the focus of Appreciative Inquiry is often the organisation, in this context the focus of Appreciative Inquiry was the team of facilitators delivering the RCN CLP.

■ Design

As a team we had worked very closely together in rolling the Programme out across Scotland. As previously stated, the Local Facilitators had been prepared for their role by means of a residential learning community at the start of our work and this had been built on with monthly individual coaching sessions, Action Learning and workshop input. In addition, at an early stage, the Local Facilitators had requested monthly team meetings where they could share their learning and discuss areas of mutual interest and concern.

We had worked on values elicitation for the team and identified our ways of working and these had been reviewed and built on during the year. At the end of this phase of the Programme it was felt to be very important for us to meet together to evaluate the impact of the Programme across Scotland and also to look at where the team was and identify how we needed to move forward to strengthen the team and our task, capitalising on the individual talents of the team members.

Following discussions, another residential learning community was organised. The aim of the week was to have some intensive time together to reflect on our experiences of running the Programme both individually and collectively and also to think about what had worked well and could be built on for the team's future. In this way we would be focussing on the team, the task and the individual (Adair, 1997)

An outline for the week was negotiated to try and ensure balance. Most of the arrangements for the week had been made via e-mail so the first day was spent looking at expectations for the week, ground-rules and ways of working. Time was also spent planning the content of the week.

The second day provided some time for the Facilitators to reflect on their experiences and come together in pairs and small groups to identify their shared learning. Appreciative Inquiry work was then undertaken on the third day in the group and this seemed to work well, given that the Facilitators had

had time to reflect on their own learning as individuals and share this with others.

The 4D Model for Appreciative Inquiry is described by Cooperrider *et al.* (1999) as a process for positive change. Appreciative Inquiry moves through four phases:

1. **Discovery phase** – appreciating and valuing the best of "what is".
2. **Dream phase** – envisioning what "might be".
3. **Design phase** – determining what "will be".
4. **Delivery phase** – planning what "will be".

Appreciative Inquiry was then used as the foundation for developing our team and our strategy for developing and sustaining the RCN CLP in Scotland. This is discussed in the following section under evaluation.

■ Evaluation

During the residential learning community the facilitators focussed on their experiences as part of a virtual team delivering the Programme. The key themes to emerge from this work became the basis for our focus as a team, guiding priorities and decisions on how work would be taken forward in the future. These are presented below under the stages of Appreciative Inquiry.

Discovery phase – appreciating and valuing the best of "what is"

- Being part of a team – it has been a "privilege with ups and downs".
- Taking risks.
- Celebrating successes.
- Seeing changes in the clinical leaders and changes for patients.
- Building relationships within the team.
- Co-coaching.
- Valuing the diversity of the team.
- Encouragement and support from each other.
- Learning from networking and political awareness.
- Affirmation of the value I add.
- Being clear about my values and living them.

Dream phase – envisioning what "might be"

- Full recognition and utilisation of skills.
- Sharing skills across organisational boundaries.

- More openness and honesty.
- A strong and cohesive team.
- Reputation spreading through out the country, recognised as a powerful resource.
- Linking-in with other existing groups.
- Influencing policy and practice, education and research.
- A consultation group.

Design phase – determining what "will be"

- Review team performance and build on this.
- Review of team meetings to maximise their effectiveness.
- Personal commitment to attend.
- Identify a vehicle for sharing/documenting expertise on the Programme.
- Publication of articles and conference presentations.
- Taking opportunities to build political awareness by shadowing

Delivery phase – planning what "will be"

At the residential learning community some planning work took place. However, it was important to us that the whole team was involved in the Appreciative Inquiry process. There were only 13 facilitators at the residential learning community while the team actually consisted of 18 members. It was decided to take this work forward to our next team meeting where the members who were absent would be able to contribute to the discussions, gain an understanding of where the work had come from and be involved in shaping our future.

At our next meeting we started off by looking again at our values using the values elicitation exercise. This helped to draw the whole team together by focussing on our shared values, and the ways of working flowed from them.

The next exercise we used was described as "The Dream Team". The purpose of this was to encourage team members to express their feelings about how they currently saw their working environment and how different they would like the future to be. The rationale for using this particular exercise was to build on the work from Appreciative Inquiry and help those not present for the original work to engage and feel involved, providing an opportunity to unlock the creative potential of all the facilitators by working together in a different way. This exercise also included a dimension designed to develop team members' personal ownership along with their ability to make necessary changes in respect of their individual role and the function of the team.

The agreed collated issues which emerged from this work, with some initial ideas for addressing them were:

- **Visioning** – statement, mission, etc.
- **Strategy** – direction, work plan.
- **Communication** – newsletter; chain e-mail; template for reporting.
- **Team meeting** – review agenda.
- **Develop negotiation skills** – workshop.
- **Celebrate achievements** – every third meeting.
- **Identify key skills in the team** – skills register, sharing skills.
- **Build in commitment to team** – challenge and support, attending and completing work, ground-rules.
- **Time to explore new ideas**
- **Develop networking and political awareness** – invite people to meeting, increase awareness of wider agenda.
- **Be louder in terms of influence**
- **Implement programme recommendations**
- **Look at role of support facilitator**
- **Evolve programme and share good practice.**

This detail was then incorporated into a document intended for use by the facilitation team called "The RCN Clinical Leadership Programme: Scottish Clinical Leadership Team Ways of Working and Strategic Direction: 2003–2005". The purpose of the document was to clarify the vision, mission, agreed ways of working, associated structures and processes. It also outlined the team's priorities and provided an action plan of what required to be done, who was going to do it and by when. The methods and time scales for reviewing and measuring the outcomes was also included.

◼ Summary and conclusions

Clear operating practices must be in place to support the building of a team's sense of purpose, particularly when geographically-dispersed (Hart & McLeod, 2002). Clarifying values and establishing ways of working which, for this team, require to reflect the transformational leadership behaviours being espoused as part of the core work, was essential. In addition, this network must sustain the Local Facilitators and promote their continuing development. Practices must also fulfil the criteria which Campton (2002) describes as the need for "mutual knowledge" or "common ground" to be established for future communication to be understood and effective, particularly pertinent when the primary medium used for communicating is electronic.

Hart & McLeod state that friendly, personal acquaintanceships are the number one contributor to productivity within a virtual team and that building relationships with peers in a virtual team is more important than in face-to-face or co-located teams:

> "Close relationships in geographically-dispersed teams are in fact important to task accomplishment, individual satisfaction and development"
>
> *(Hart and McLeod, 2002)*

However, they warn that these relationships will not grow serendipitously but require mechanisms to be in place to ensure frequent exchange of relevant information in order to develop a shared meaning.

Over and above being an opportunity for the team members to come together to work in a safe and informal environment conducive to building relationships, the residential learning community proved to be a rich learning experience. Completing the Appreciative Inquiry work as part of that experience, and the supporting work which followed, enabled this team to look to the future by reflecting and building-on the work of the past in a positive way.

As stated by Cooperrider and Barrett (1990), discussing our team performance in a structured way which emphasised the achievements and focussed on the exciting possibilities for individuals, the team and the RCN CLP resulted in the compilation of a document which clarifies the expectations of all members of the team. It provided an exciting plan for the future in keeping with our vision of advancing excellence in clinical leadership across the NHS in Scotland.

■ References

Adair, J (1999) *Decision-Making and Problem-Solving*. London, Institute of Personnel & Development.

Alimo-Metcalfe, B. & Alban-Metcalfe, J. (2003), Stamp of greatness, *Health Service Journal*, (26 June), pp 28–32.

Bennis, W. & Nanus, B. (1985) *Leaders: The Strategies for Taking Charge*. New York, Harper & Row.

Black, S. (2000) Taking the lead, *Nursing Standard*, Vol. 14, No. 44, p. 13.

Carlowe, J. & Cole, A. (1997) Leading player, *Nursing Times*, Vol. 93, No. 42, pp 12–13.

Cooperrider, D. & Barrett, F. (1990) Generative metaphor intervention: a new approach for working with systems divided, *Journal of Applied Behavioral Science*, Vol. 26, No. 2, pp 25–38.

Cooperrider, D., Sorenson, P., Whitney, D. & Yaeger, T (1999) *Appreciative Inquiry: Rethinking Human Organization Towards A Positive Theory of Change*. Champagne, Illinois, Stipes Publishing Company.

Campton, C. (2002) Finding common ground in dispersed collaboration, *Organisational Dynamics,* Vol. 30, No. 4, pp 356–367.

Cunningham, G. & Kitson, A. (1997) *A Journey to Patient Centred Leadership.* London, RCN Publications.

Cunningham, G. & Kitson, A. (2000a) An evaluation of The RCN Clinical Leadership Programme: Part 1, *Nursing Standard,* Vol. 15, No. 12, pp 34–37.

Cunningham, G. & Kitson, A. (2000b) An evaluation of The RCN Clinical Leadership Programme: Part 2, *Nursing Standard,* Vol. 15, No. 13, pp 34–40.

Cunningham, G., Large, S., Kitson, A., Allen, E., Lister, S. & Nash, S. (2002) *Summary Evaluation Report for Phase 2 of the RCN Clinical Leadership Programme.* London, RCN.

De Geest, S., Claessens, P., Longerich, H. & Schubert, M. (2003) Transformational leadership: worth the investment, *European Journal of Cardiovascular Nursing,* No. 2, pp 3–5.

Department of Health (1999) *Making a Difference: Strengthening the Nursing, Midwifery and Health Visiting Contribution to Health and Healthcare.* London, DoH.

Department of Health (2000) *The NHS Plan: a Plan for Investment: a Plan for Reform.* London, DoH.

Faugier J. & Woolnough, H. (2002) Valuing "voices from below", *Journal of Nursing Management,* Vol. 10, pp 315–320.

Goodwin, N. (2000) Leadership and the UK Health Service, *Health Policy,* No. 51, pp 49–60.

Goldberg, R. (2001) Implementing a professional development system through Appreciative Inquiry, *Leadership and Organization Development Journal,* Vol. 22, No.2, pp 56–61.

Govier, I. (2004) Advocating excellence in leadership, *Nursing Management,* Vol.10, No. 9, pp 13–15.

Hambridge, P. (1997) Learning practical leadership, *Paediatric Nursing,* Vol. 9, No. 10, pp. 6–7.

Hart, R. & McLeod, P. (2002) Rethinking team building in geographically dispersed teams: one message at a time, *Organisational Dynamics,* Vol. 31, No. 4, pp 352–361.

Kouzes, J. & Posner, B. (1997) *The Leadership Challenge.* San Fransisco, Jossey-Bass Inc.

Mackenzie, H. & Cunningham, G. (2002) *RCN Clinical Leadership Programme – Evaluation of Phase 3 of the Programme in Scotland.* RCN Scotland

Mahoney, J. (2001) Leadership skills for the 21st century, *Journal of Nursing Management,* Vol. 9, pp 269–271.

Scottish Executive (2000) *Our National Health – A Plan For Action, A Plan For Change.* Edinburgh, Scottish Executive.

Scottish Executive (2001) *Caring For Scotland – The Strategy for Nursing and Midwifery in Scotland.* Edinburgh, Scottish Executive.

Scottish Executive (2003) *Partnership for Care.* Edinburgh, Scottish Executive.

Scottish Executive (2004) *Leadership Development Framework.* Edinburgh, Scottish Executive.

Simons, F. (2003a) Clinical leadership: part 1: key components of the programme, *Professional Nurse,* Vol. 18, No. 11, pp 656–657.

Simons, F. (2003b) Clinical leadership: part 2: transferring leadership, *Professional Nurse*, Vol. 18, No. 12, pp 716–717.

Simons, F. (2003c) Clinical leadership: part 3: how to foster a leading role for everyone, *Professional Nurse*, Vol. 19, No. 1, pp 56–57.

Trofino, J. (1995) Transformational leadership in health care, *Nursing Management*, Vol. 26, No. 8, pp. 42–47.

Whitney, D. (1998) Let's change the subject and change our organization: an Appreciative Inquiry approach to organizational change. *Career Development International.* Vol. 3, No. 7, pp 314–319.

Zeus, P. & Skiffington, S. (2002) *The Coaching at Work Toolkit: A Complete Guide to Techniques and Practices.* New South Wales, Australia, McGraw-Hill.

CHAPTER

7

"What's the best day you've ever had at work?" Appreciative Inquiry at the Manchester Heart Centre

Robin Alfred and Robin Shohet

These and similar questions lie at the heart of Appreciative Inquiry, a process with which we have been working in Manchester Heart Centre (MHC), part of the Central Manchester & Manchester Children's University Hospitals NHS Trust, over an 18-month period. Starting with stories of great days and moments at work and teasing-out the values and relationships that helped make these happen, an Appreciative Inquiry approach enables future visions and strategy to be built on the inspiration of the past. This case study demonstrates how working with Appreciative Inquiry in Manchester Heart Centre has helped create a sea-change in culture and behaviour within the Centre, liberating creativity and passion for the work.

We will also outline each of the steps in the process so that you can guide yourself and others through it if you wish.

■ June 2003 – the journey begins

It is midsummer, and we are sitting with five members of the Senior Management Team (SMT) in an airless basement of Manchester Royal Infirmary. We have been asked to facilitate a 3-day Leadership Development event and have chosen to focus on Appreciative Inquiry for the first day. We start by explaining the model:

The first step is **Discovery**, which involves looking at what has already been working well in the system. We started with paired interviews in which each person asks the other a set of predetermined questions:

1. Think of a time when you felt good about what you were doing, perhaps a time when your contribution really made a difference. Tell the story about that time as if it were happening now. Who was involved? What was your role? How were you effective? What was the response around you? What skills were you using?

2a Without being too humble, what do you most value about yourself?

2b What do you most value about your work?

2c What do you most value about the Heart Centre?

3. What values are important to you in the designing and delivering of your work?

4. Imagine you are describing Manchester Heart Centre to a friend. How would you describe its essence or its unique life-giving force?

5. Imagine it is 2006. All the changes you have wanted to see in the Heart Centre have happened. Describe MHC now. How have these changes come about? What has been your contribution? What aspect of the change are you most delighted with?

(We invite you, the reader, to pause and reflect on these questions for yourself, applying them to your own work situation.)

Following the interviews each person "introduced" their partner by sharing their responses to the questions. Taking one question at a time, as each person shared their partner's responses, others noticed key words, phrases and images and called them out to be recorded on a flip chart by a third person.

As the stories were shared, there was a buzz in the room; people were touched and sometimes surprised. We have always been similarly moved at how people who have worked together for many years start to see each other in a new light as they learn what really touches and inspires the other. Much of the power of Appreciative Inquiry lies in simply giving permission for positive stories to be told and heard. We call it *"positive gossip"*.

The responses to Questions 2, 3, 4 and 5 were then also shared and key words transcribed onto large post-it notes. This completed the Discovery phase.

We then invited our five managers to begin the **Dream** phase (which builds on current successes and takes some of their contributing factors into the future) by placing the post-its on each of five flip chart pieces of paper (one for each set of questions) on the wall. We invited them to stand back and notice; to cluster phrases and images that were related; to add new ones if need be and to move Post-Its from one sheet to another. Essentially we were creating a space for more intuitive, creative right-brain interpretations of the material. To further enhance this we provided drawing materials and invited the participants to draw, individually or collectively, the essence of what they saw before them.

While some of the team hesitated, one hitherto reticent team member grabbed a marker pen and shouted *"This is how I see it!"* and started to draw. Others cluster around her and joined in. Striking images emerge.

Finally we asked the team to craft a "Provocative Proposition" (PP) – a statement that represented a shared vision and was drawn out of the stories and values unearthed in the Discovery phase. We told them the PP needs to be:

- Specific
- Achievable
- Collaborative
- Challenging
- Inspiring.

They come back with:

> We are determined, and committed, to deliver high quality patient focused care, in a culture of openness, togetherness and passion, by teams who are valued for the work they do.

Our ultimate aim is to achieve international recognition

We closed the day with a round of feedback and appreciation.

On the following day, we arrived to find a more congenial and open atmosphere. Yet the session started with one member spontaneously declaring that:

> "Yesterday was all very nice, but there are some real issues to deal with here. I don't want to gloss over those."

The implication was that our first day had been pleasant froth but nothing more. She went on to describe her relationship with her manager (also in the room) which was characterised by tension and which felt almost unworkable. We facilitated a dialogue between the two which led to, firstly, a more conscious understanding of one another, and secondly, a deep appreciation. The relationship appeared transformed (and at the time of writing, some 18 months later, still is).

Lead Nurse/Modern Matron Anne Porter said:

> 'That was the turning point, finding out what gives someone that buzz. It made me look at the person rather than where they are in the hierarchy.'

Some people may imagine that Appreciative Inquiry, with its emphasis on the positive, can exclude or marginalise conflict. This example shows that this is not the case. Where conflict needs to emerge, the Appreciative Inquiry approach helps create a positive and appreciative context within which conflict can be expressed and transformed safely, with the supportive awareness of the team.

Our 3-day training event moved on to look at how the team can start to **Design** and **Deliver** some of the key aspects of the Provocative Proposition, including the hosting of an Appreciative Inquiry day for up to 50 people drawn from a variety of teams and disciplines within the Heart Centre. This was to be held early the following year. We also make an arrangement for a follow-up meeting with the Management Team in September.

■ September/November 2003 – follow up

A soft autumn day in September with characteristic Manchester drizzle saw us meeting our increasingly cohesive Management Team to look at ways of working with stress and to check on progress with regard to Appreciative Inquiry. We noticed that team members were taking more responsibility for the well-being of the team and of each other, and were no longer relying on the Director to take the lead. We attributed this, at least in part, to the way Appreciative Inquiry involves everyone equally and encourages mutual ownership of the Appreciative Inquiry process. We agreed to meet again in November – this time to review MHC's Organisation Development Programme, of which Appreciative Inquiry is a key component.

One of the reasons that Appreciative Inquiry is so effective in Manchester Heart Centre is that it is part of a multi-faceted approach to organisation development and culture change. A core component is the dynamic and visionary leadership of its Director, who not only models the humane, approachable and appreciative style he wants to propagate through the Centre, but also employs trainers, coaches and consultants to match. One of these consultants, Jadzia Kopiel, had paved the way for Appreciative Inquiry through highly effective coaching and training on such issues as work/life balance and creativity.

In November, using semi-structured individual interviews and group dialogue, we reviewed the progress that had been made. It was striking how positive and enthusiastic everyone was about being in the team and about the changes that were underway.

Typical phrases that characterise "before" and "after" were:

Before	After
Feeling isolated	Openness
Feeling checked up on	Approachability
In the dark	Empowerment
Cliques	Professionalism
Favouritism	Honesty

We asked for **images** that might encapsulate this shift. Here are some responses:

> **"Storm moving to tranquillity"**
>
> *"House of straw to a brick house with firm structures"*
>
> *"A VW before (quite efficient and not very inviting) and now it is a 2CV (laid back, not quite as image-conscious, and gets the job done."*

Some **quotes** that support this:

> *"He's very visible. I like that very much. Anthony is interested in everyone. You can't get away with stuff."*
>
> *"Now we seem less focussed on task, but the task gets done anyway!"*
>
> *"More business-like, but not at the expense of humanity."*

One important finding, highlighted in the last two of these quotes, is that what is often perceived as the need for a trade-off between humanity and efficiency, or between task and process, is actually a false dichotomy. We understood that, despite or because of taking time out for staff development purposes, the Centre's targets had all been achieved, some considerably earlier than planned for.

Team members described the current culture as:

- Being able to say what you really feel.
- Being honest.
- Being able to make mistakes and have that be OK!
- Becoming a learning team
- Appreciation
- Trust
- "I am comfortable about me"

We closed this upbeat and buoyant day by agreeing a date in February 2004 for an Appreciative Inquiry event for up to 50 people drawn from a variety of teams and disciplines across the Heart Centre.

■ February, 2004 – bringing others on board

In February 2004 some 35 people gathered, slightly thrown to be invited to sit in a circle without the usual protection of a desk. *"Who are these people?"* and *"What is this all about?"* are the unspoken questions. After a round of introductions, we explained the whole Appreciative Inquiry cycle of Discover, Dream, Design, Deliver (see Figures 7.1 and 7.2), saving the more detailed instructions for later.

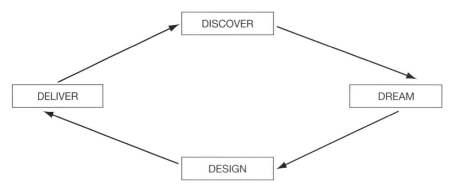

Figure 7.1 Appreciative Inquiry – methodology

DISCOVER
- Interview each other using prepared questionnaire (see above: 5 questions on pages 97 and 98)
- Report back – tell each other's stories
- Back into small groups/pairs – create key words/ideas on Post-its

DREAM
- Place Post-its on 4 flipchart papers: stories, values, what is the project's life-giving force? Dreams
- Cluster the Post-its
- Draw the essence of what you see on the flipcharts
- Create a "provocative proposition" from the drawing

DESIGN
- Design the means of achieving the provocative proposition (i.e. next steps. Could be seen as a path with the PP at the end point – what are the next steps you need to take along the path to meet that goal?)

DELIVER
- Set targets, timelines, resources (human and other) that you need to deliver this.

Figure 7.2 Appreciative Inquiry inquiry cycle

In the opening circle it became clear that around 80% of the attendees were from what (to us) was a mysterious unit called the "Cath (i.e Catheter) Lab". In order to build team cohesion and to add further meaning to their experience of the Appreciative Inquiry process, we divided the participants into six groups, based on their respective work areas, including several for the ubiquitous "Cath Lab" staff.

Once again, the atmosphere both lightened and deepened as stories of inspirational days and moments filled the air. The Discovery phase blended into the Dreaming stage as Post-its were generated with key words and images on them, which were then clustered. As each group started to work on the crafting of their Provocative Proposition point, we invited them to identify both a core theme around which they would focus their PP, and to choose a name for their group. This injects an opportunity for humour and creativity.

The results were impressive. The Provocative Propositions generated by each group are shown in Figure 7.3.

Name: Piston broke
Theme: Building team atmosphere
Within the Manchester Heart Centre is a dedicated, flexible and efficient multidisciplinary group which promotes trust, respect and a positive mental attitude, encouraging its team players to deliver high standards of quality care creating an enjoyable working atmosphere.

Name: Different strokes
Theme: Communication
Communication in the Manchester Heart Centre is a priority. It is personal yet backed up by modern and efficient technological systems. The staff work collaboratively to ensure a smooth and efficient patient pathway. Continuous feedback of information throughout the Heart Centre ensures total patient care.

Name: Ali's army
Theme: Communication
The communication network within the MHC is so effective that everyone feels part of one team, having an awareness of each other's roles, needs and aspirations. As a result they provide the highest standards of care for every patient that journeys through the Heart Centre.

Name: The communicators
Theme: Communication
MHC is a centre of excellence with commitment to improving communication at all levels. We are dedicated to the developing, emerging needs of all staff with evolving technologies. We are proud to lead in improving and sharing communication skills across all boundaries.

Name: Clueless
Theme: Patient care
The MHC is committed to a multidisciplinary approach to individually focused total patient care, respecting cultural and religious differences. On a daily basis, not only do we provide every patient, from every walk of life, the respect, privacy and dignity they deserve; but we also offer support, information and advice to patients and their loved ones.

Name: TPR
Theme: Trust, People, Respect
Through our behaviour, conduct and personal interactions with others, it is evident that *Trust* and *Respect* are the foundations which underpin the fundamental daily activities of the MHC.

Figure 7.3 Provocative Propositions

It is interesting to note that communication was the key issue for three of the six groups. Appreciative Inquiry is well placed to address this, as people are already meeting and speaking across disciplines and in an open and mutually supportive way.

Framing the PPs in the present tense also served to bring them into the room as if the Centre is already working in this way. The PPs started to function as affirmations.

We closed the day by agreeing to convene one month later, asking each group to commit to meeting in the interim to work on the Design phase of the process (i.e. to create a clear pathway to the realisation of the Provocative Proposition). The participants decide that these groups should each be facilitated by a member of the Senior Management Team, who we had arranged to train for this purpose the following day.

When we met with the SMT the following day, they appreciates how deeply they now trusted one another. They were prepared to role-play being facilitators and demonstrate their understanding of Appreciative Inquiry in front of one another – something that they would have baulked at only six months before.

■ March 2004 – including the cardiologists

One of the conspicuous absences in the process so far had been that of the consultant cardiologists, who had been invited to participate but had so far not made an appearance. We agreed with the Director that their participation, or at least their awareness and understanding of the process, was vital. Indeed, reference to their ways of working, and in particular their style of communication, had been made several times in the meetings so far. We also saw that, in order to bring about the whole-system culture change that this Appreciative Inquiry process is geared towards, all parts of MHC needed to be involved.

To facilitate this involvement, we interviewed each of the cardiologists individually, both to build our relationship with them, and to ascertain each of their perspectives as to what issues could usefully be addressed in their team. These interviews were designed to pave the way towards a day of team-building that we would facilitate and which would use Appreciative Inquiry to open the door to dialogues about leadership and other issues.

There was considerable wariness about the day – and about our ability to hold their process and relationships – because of poor prior experience of such facilitated days, and a consequent understandable wish to let sleeping dogs lie. Once we embarked on the Discovery phase, however, using paired interviews, the atmosphere shifted to one of curiosity and interest. Again, we were struck that such a simple structure creates profound shifts. As the day moved on we used brainstorming and in-depth discussion to examine key questions of leadership and relationship – these potentially difficult conversations being made immeasurably easier by the Appreciative Inquiry opening.

We also took the opportunity to describe the Appreciative Inquiry process that the rest of Manchester Heart Centre was embarked upon and we invited the cardiologists to participate the following day, when we were re-convening with the 35 people already engaged in the process.

Lead Cardiologist, Professor Clifford Garratt said:

> "As consultant cardiologists, we were all fairly sceptical; we thought it sounded very touchy-feely. We were uncertain we would get any benefit from it, but there is no doubt that we learnt a great deal about each other's aspirations for the department and it was very useful in terms of communication between consultant staff and achieving a set of common goals. I would recommend it."

■ March 2004 – the moment of truth!

Would anyone turn up? Would the participants have done the work they agreed to do last time we met? What if the momentum had completely disappeared? Can this process work in the NHS, given all the pressure on time? Slowly the room filled. So at least the people had come – but what would they present?

First up were "The Communicators" who give a stunning 15-slide Powerpoint presentation detailing a strategy for achieving their Provocative Proposition. It was heartening to see that they had already started to put things into practice. Some extracts from their presentation are shown in Figures 7.4 and 7.5.

There was loud applause and the group took a bow. We were all impressed and encouraged that so much had been achieved since our first meeting only five weeks before.

One by one, each group presented and the results were similarly impressive. By the end of the morning we had seen six powerful presentations of Provocative Propositions that were already making a difference within and between teams, and frequently having an impact on patient care – the increasingly visible bottom- line for all of the groups.

The TPR (Trust, People, Respect) group comprised the Senior Management Team. The Centre Director had started to make people aware of their Provocative Proposition, and of the emphasis his team were now placing on cultivating attitudes of trust and respect, by including it on Management Team agendas and in his e-mails. Perhaps more importantly, he

Figure 7.4 Channels of communication

- To introduce information technology as being an essential basic skill to the MHC.
- To ensure that information technology is a compulsory part of the learning and development of each staff member.
- To ensure that each member of staff has access to the trust e-mail system and is present on the relevant mailing list.
- To ensure that those members of staff can use the Cardex information control system which is essential for their jobs.
- To ensure that members of staff are aware that the Heart Centre IT team exists and that it can offer training and support to the users.
- To be able to offer structured training courses. There should be regular slots every week so that there is a continuity of the training/learning process.
- To be able to offer one-to-one training to members of staff if they want to learn IT in more depth.
- To concentrate on staff members who have not received any training so far, especially in the Ward areas and Cath labs.
- To be able to offer accredited recognised training courses to staff. This can be beneficial for the long term retention of learning and the staff will also be motivated and feel a sense of achievement.
- To be able to offer support to staff who are doing accredited courses externally.
- To be able to publish the resources on the intranet, and to design interactive courses on the intranet to enable staff to do their courses independently.

Figure 7.5 Long-term aims (emerged from Appreciative Inquiry)

was also calling people to account when they fell short of the PP and acted towards one another in ways that showed lack of respect or trust. The change was tangible, with one main grade staff member volunteering that the attitudes of senior staff to the main grade nurses had been completely transformed.

Senior radiographer, Sue Evans, did not attend the first away-day in February, but noticed an immediate change in those who did. She said:

> "They were being polite to each other, everybody kept thanking each other for doing things. It was so different from normal!"

In the afternoon we gave time for the groups to meet and plan their next steps. We concluded the day by inviting one or more representatives from each group to volunteer to form a seventh group that would work on drafting a Provocative Proposition for MHC as a whole.

This group was mandated by the rest to do this and started its deliberations in a "fish-bowl" setting, sitting in a circle in the middle of the group, with a couple of empty chairs so that others could come in and out and contribute as they wished.

We agreed to meet in three months to review how all seven groups were getting on.

■ July 2004 – the Heineken Effect

At this stage, we wanted to reach the parts of MHC that other processes had failed to reach – we jokingly call it the Heineken Effect – and to review the progress so far.

The MHC Provocative Proposition group reported back. While it had been hard to find time to meet they had managed to do so and had created a Provocative Proposition:

> The MHC is a vibrant and progressive environment, delivering quality patient care, ensuring privacy and dignity at all times. We are enthusiastic, friendly professionals who trust, respect and value one another, regardless of position. Through effective communication we are one team with one goal – "To be the best".

Each of the original groups reported back on its progress, and we were delighted to find that the momentum had continued.

In the afternoon we shared our vision of how this process could spread through the whole of MHC. We wished to invite all those who wanted to, and to take on the responsibility of convening a Discovery group of up to ten people, and facilitating the Discovery phase of Appreciative Inquiry through paired interviews. Seven people volunteered to do this straight away.

We distributed two handouts – one outlining the Appreciative Inquiry process, and one offering "Guidelines For Leading A First Stage Appreciative Inquiry Group" (see Appendix). We divided the remaining participants into seven groups and the volunteers practiced their Appreciative Inquiry descriptions and group facilitation. This process mirrored that offered to the Senior

Management Team some four months previously. We were now training main grade MHC staff to be facilitators and owners of the Appreciative Inquiry process. The seven became twelve as other participants were encouraged to take on this role and were offered the opportunity to facilitate in pairs. Our plan is to have all those who have taken part attend the next gathering, potentially an Appreciative Inquiry event for 150 MHC staff to be held in December, 2004, though we will need to make sure we are not being over-ambitious. It may be better to build an Appreciative Inquiry momentum with other parts of MHC first and then move to a larger event some time in 2005.

■ Conclusion

We started working with MHC in June 2003 and our most recent meeting was July, 2004. In that time we have watched how scepticism has given way to optimism. This is good in itself, but we and the participants were especially pleased to see how much this "feel good factor" had already translated into working practices. As we were writing this article we rang one of the Senior Management Team to find the Centre-wide Provocative Proposition drawn up in July 2004. *"No problem"*, she said. *"It's up on my wall"*, and she e-mailed it to us straight away.

Appreciative Inquiry is still a "work in progress". It is not a quick fix or a set of techniques guaranteed to achieve measurable targets, though this chapter shows that it assists with meeting targets too. It *is* a way of looking at the world which moves its focus from problems to opportunities, and as such helps to generate positive, achievable outcomes. It requires a high degree of commitment, in terms of time and the release of staff, and we wish to appreciate the vision of the Director and of the Senior Management Team who employed us and Appreciative Inquiry as part of a multi-faceted approach to culture change in the workplace.

Several times we felt tested and we kept our belief that if the right circumstances are created, people naturally want to give of their best and to help others to do the same. In a blame- and fear-driven culture this belief can seem naive, but all the work that we have done with Appreciative Inquiry, not just in Manchester Heart Centre but in schools, which are also stressful places, has confirmed our belief.

In this chapter we have taken you through our work in some detail in order to demystify the process. Appreciative Inquiry's foundation of appreciative interviews can easily be practised – and we encourage you to start talking to people in this way. You will be amazed at the effect of simply listening and telling positive stories. When *was* your best day at work?

Appendix: Manchester Heart Centre

Guidelines for leading a first stage Appreciative Inquiry group

1. We recommend that the group last **one hour**, as people might find it difficult to commit for more.
2. Because time is short we suggest you start promptly and also finish on time. If you would like to socialise, you can offer tea, coffee, biscuits etc. either before or after, but keep the full hour for the AI.
3. We suggest **10 people per group** – recruit them as you wish.
4. After welcoming and thanking them for coming, start with a round of names and roles in MHC, and then share your own experiences of AI (5 minutes total).
5. You can then continue with some of the basic ideas:
   - AI focuses on looking at what works and building on that.
   - AI is not problem-focused.
   - From the positive stories and experiences we hear, we then generate a vision of the future and how it can be.
   - The last stages involve grounding this vision, by designing steps that need to be taken to realise it.
6. Then explain that in this hour you will be focusing on the first part of the process only. This will feed into a day to which everyone is invited, where they will move through the subsequent stages.
7. The hour you are facilitating is about the first stage – the conversations. These will be 15 minutes each way (equal time is important) and you will call time at the end of the first conversation. Remind the "interviewers" that they are there to listen, not to put their own ideas in, and they need to record what the other says, making sure to keep it positive even if the other person wants to drift into stories where things haven't worked.
8. "Interviewers" need to remember that they are the keepers of their partner's stories and that they will be feeding-back their partner's story to the rest of the group, so it is important to have a feel for it.
9. When the interviews are done, ask how it was both talking and listening, and invite people to share their partner's story.
10. Note down on a flip chart any key words, phrases, or themes that you hear in each story.
11. Read back what you have on the flip chart, and check if the group feels it is accurate, and if anyone has anything else to add.
12. Finally, ask if you can keep the sheet, and explain that the information will be part of a project for the whole of MHC.

Outline timing – one hour

Welcome and thanks for coming	1 minute
Round of names, roles and your minutes	5 minutes
Experience of AI	
Outline the process and the focus of the hour	10 minutes
Distribute interview protocols	
Pair up	
Stories told and listened to	30 minutes
Sharing each other's stories	10 minutes
Check key words, themes etc	3 minutes
Thanks for coming and see you at the follow-up event	1 minute

■ Bibliography

Covey. S. (1994) *The Seven Habits of Highly Effective People*. London, Simon & Schuster

Edmonstone, J. & Havergal, M. (1995) The death (and rebirth?) of organisation development, *Health Manpower Management*, Vol. 21, No. 1, pp 28-33

Elliott, C. (1999) *Locating the Energy for Change: an Introduction to Appreciative Inquiry*. Winnipeg, International Institute for Sustainable Development.

French, W. & Bell, C. (1999) *Organization Development: Behavioral Science Interventions for Organization Improvement*. 6th edition, Upper Saddle River, NJ, Prentice-Hall.

Garvey, R. & Williamson, W. (2002) *Beyond Knowledge Management: Dialogue, Creativity and the Corporate Curriculum*. Harlow, Pearson Education.

Peters, T. & Waterman, H. (1982) *In Search of Excellence: Lessons from America's Best-Run Companies*. New York, Harper & Row.

Rittel, H. & Webber, M. (1973) Dilemmas in a general theory of planning, *Policy Sciences*, Vol. 4, No. 1, pp 155–159.

Further reading on Appreciative Inquiry

Anderson, H., Cooperrider, D., Gergen, K., Gergen, M., McNamee, S. & Whitney, D. (2001) *The Appreciative Organisation*. Taos Institute Publications.

Baker, A. & Wright, M. (2004) Using AI to initiate stakeholder interactions in healthcare, *AI Practitioner* (May), pp 30–31.

Barrett, F. (1995) Creating appreciative learning cultures, *Organisational Dynamics*, Vol. 24, No. 2, pp 36–49.

Barrett, F. & Cooperrider, D. (1990) Generative metaphor intervention: a new approach for working with systems divided by conflict and caught in defensive perception, *Journal of Applied Behavioral Science*, Vol. 26, No. 2, pp 219–239.

Barrett, F., Thomas, G. & Hocevar, S. (1995) The central role of discourse in large-scale change: a social construction perspective, *Journal of Applied Behavioral Science*, Vol. 31, No. 3, pp 352–372.

Bunker, B. (1990) Appreciating Diversity And Modifying Organisational Cultures: Men And Women At Work. In: Srivastva, S. & Cooperrider, D. (eds) *Appreciative Management and Leadership: The Power of Positive Thought and Action in Organisations*. San Francisco, Jossey-Bass.

Bushe, G. (1998) Appreciative Inquiry with teams, *Organisation Development Journal*, Vol.16, No. 3, pp 41–50.

Bushe, G. (1998) *Five Theories of Change Embedded in Appreciative Inquiry*, Paper presented at 18th Annual World Congress of Organisation Development, Dublin, Ireland.

Bushe, G. (1997) *Attending to Others: Interviewing Appreciatively*. Vancouver, British Columbia, Discovery & Design Inc.

Bushe, G. (1995) Advances in Appreciative Inquiry as an organisation development intervention, *Organisation Development Journal*, Vol.13, No.3, pp 14–22.

Bushe, G. & Coetzer, G. (1995) Appreciative Inquiry as a team development intervention: a controlled experiment, *Journal of Applied Behavioral Science*, Vol.31, No.1, pp 19–31.

Bushe, G. & Pitman, T. (1991) Appreciative process: a method for transformational change, *Organisation Development Practitioner*, September, pp 1–4.

Cooperrrider, D. (1996) The "child" as agent of inquiry, *Organisation Development Practitioner*, Vol. 28, Nos. 1 & 2, pp 5–11.

Cooperrider, D. (1996) Resources for getting Appreciative Inquiry started: an example OD proposal, *Organisation Development Practitioner*, Vol. 28, Nos. 1 & 2, pp. 23–33.

Cooperrider, D. (1990) Positive image, positive action: the affirmative basis of organising. In: Srivastva, S. & Cooperrider, D. (eds) *Appreciative Management and Leadership: the Power of Positive Thought and Action in Organisations*, San Francisco, Jossey-Bass.

Cooperrrider, D, Fry, R., Barrett, F., Seiling, J. & Whitney, D. (2001) *Appreciative Inquiry and Organisational Transformation: Reports from the Field*. Greenwood Press.

Cooperrider, D. & Srivastva, S. (1987) Appreciative Inquiry in organisational life. In: Pasmore, W. & Woodman, R. (eds) *Research in Organisation Change and Development*, Vol.1, No. 1, pp 129–169.

Cooperrider, D. Sorenson, P., Yaeger, T. & Whitney, D. (2001) *Appreciative Inquiry: an Emerging Direction for Organisation Development*. Stipes Publishing.

Cooperrider, D., Sorenson, P., Whitney, D. & Yaeger, T. (eds), (1999) *Appreciative Inquiry: Rethinking Human Organisation Toward a Positive Theory of Change*. Champagne, Illinois, Stipes Publishing.

Cooperrider, D. & Whitney, D. (1999) *Appreciative Inquiry*. San Francisco, Berrett-Koehlet.

Cooperrider, D. & Whitney, D. (1998) The Appreciative Inquiry Summit: overview and application. *Employment Relations Today*, Summer, pp 17–28.

Elliott, C. (1999) *Locating the Energy for Change: an Introduction to Appreciative Inquiry*. Winnipeg, International Institute for Sustainable Development.

Fry, R., Barrett, F., Seiling, J. & Whitney, D. (eds) (2002) *Appreciative Inquiry and Organisational Transformation: Reports from the Field*. Quorum, Westport, CT.

Fry, R., Cooperrider, D., Whitney, D. & Starvos, J. (2004) *Appreciative Inquiry Handbook: the First of a Series Workbooks for Leaders of Change*. Contemporary Books.

Goldberg, R. (2001) Implementing a professional development system through Appreciative Inquiry. *Leadership & Organisation Development Journal*, Vol. 22, No. 2, pp 56–61.

Hammond, S. (1998) *The Thin Book of Appreciative Inquiry*, 2nd edition, Plano, Texas, Thin Book Publishing.

Hammond, S. & Royal, C. (1998) *Lessons from the Field: Applying Appreciative Inquiry*. Plano, Texas, Practical Press.

Liebling, A., Price, D. & Elliott, C. (1999), Appreciative Inquiry and relationships in prison, *Punishment and Society*, Vol. 1, No. 1, pp 67–94.

Magruder-Watkins, J & Mohr, B. (2000) *Appreciative Inquiry: Change at the Speed of Imagination*, San Francisco, Jossey-Bass.

Mantel, M. & Ludema, J. (2000) From local conversations to global change: experiencing the worldwide web effect of Appreciative Inquiry, *Organizational Development Journal*, Vol. 18, No. 2 (Summer), pp 42–53.

Mellish, E. (2000) *Appreciative Inquiry at Work*. Mellish & Associates.

Mellish, E. (1999), Appreciative Inquiry, *Training Journal*, November, pp 12–15.

Mohr, B., Whitney, D. & Griffin, T. (2003) *The Appreciative Inquiry Summit: A Practitioner's Guide For Leading Large Group Change*. Berrett-Koehler Publishers.

Pradhan, R. (2004) The transformative power of appreciative conversations, *AI Practitioner* (February), pp 19–24.

Reed, J., Pearson, P., Douglas, B., Swinburne, S. & Wilding, H. (2002) Going home from hospital: an Appreciative Inquiry study, *Health & Social Care in the Community*, Vol. 10, No. 1, pp 36–45.

Ricketts, M. & Willis, J. (2001) *Experience Appreciative Inquiry: A Practitioner's Guide to Integrating Appreciative Inquiry with Experiential Learning*. Taos Institute Publications.

Schiller, M. Holland, B. & Riley, D. (eds) (2001) *Appreciative Leaders: In the Eye of the Beholder*. Taos Institute Publications.

Srivastva, S. & Cooperrider, D. (eds)(1990) *Appreciative Management and Leadership: The Power of Positive Thought and Action in Organisations*. San Francisco, Jossey-Bass.

Torres, C. (2001) *The Appreciative Facilitator: A Handbook for Facilitators and Teachers*. Learning Unlimited Corporation.

Watkins, J. & Cooperrider, D. (1998) Appreciative Inquiry: a transformative paradigm. *Organisation Development Practitioner*, Vol. 32, No.1, pp 6–12.

Whitney, D. (1998) Let's change the subject and change our organisation: an Appreciative Inquiry approach to organisational change. *Career Development International*, Vol. 3, No. 7, pp 314–319.

Whitney, D. & Schau, C. (1998) Appreciative Inquiry: an innovative process for organisation change. *Employment Relations Today*, Spring.

Whitney, D. Cooperrider, D. & Kaplan, B. (2001) *An Encyclopedia of Positive Questions: Volume One: Using Appreciative Inquiry to Bring Out the Best in Your Organisation*. Lakeshore Communications.

Whitney, D. & Trosten-Bloom, A. (2003) *The Power of Appreciative Inquiry: A Practical Guide to Positive Change,* Berrett-Koehler Publishers.

Williams, R. (1996) Survey guided Appreciative Inquiry: a case study. *Organisation Development Practitioner*, Vol. 28, Nos. 1 & 2, pp 43–51.

Wood, S. (2004) Creating a positive future for nursing using Appreciative Inquiry, *AI Practitioner* (February), pp 12–18.

Index